MIKE MALLOY

COLORED ICE CREAM

and Other Stories

First edition

This book was professionally typeset on Reedsy.
Find out more at reedsy.com

Dedication

To my son Christopher and my daughter Molly: The unqualified love you have given me throughout your lives has been the power from which I draw everything. And to my wife Kathy for hours of reading and suggesting corrections as this book progressed.

Contents

Foreword

Politically, the year 2016 was a total mind-fuck for me. It was like seeing a repeat of a particularly terrifying movie: I knew how it was going to end, but it still was stupefyingly scary.

Months of watching the Republican Party's Presidential Primary "debates," - in truth, a stream of demonstrable political stupidity - was partly responsible for my sense of approaching doom. The candidates were a self-selected crowd of religious nuts, extremists, tea party babblers, white supremacists, and one barely literate neo-fascist sociopath whose ever-expanding narcissism was momentarily sated by seeing his name in huge (gold) letters high above the tiny people in the street below. But those huge letters were no longer enough for the psychopath's voracious ego. He could hear the voices calling his name, telling him it was his time, the perfect time for *President Donald J. Trump!*

So, yeah, I had reached the absolute break point, a near hysteria that left me unable to speak in coherent sentences when the topic was presidential politics or the morally flat-lined candidates, chiselers all, who had nothing to offer the American people except lies, deceptions, and threats that, in a different time, would have gotten them dragged to the gates of the city and stoned to death.

It was like an unstoppable virus that returns again and again to make millions of people sick and cause some to die, this *I-wanna-be- your-President-and-save-you-from-unimaginable-liberal-evil* Republican Party circle-jerk. Every four years they reappear, sometimes the same ones, older and grayer but still world-class assholes, along with a squalling, spitting handful of newcomers who have grown to adulthood on a steady diet of the right-wing lies and distortions that erupt daily from right-wing media, flooding across the fruited plain like a backed-up, overflowing public toilet. These crazed newbies – their emotional and intellectual growth stunted and disfigured - spend most of their time as candidates trying to out-Nazi the other presidential wannabes while insisting to anyone listening they are, in fact, family-loving, god-fearing, Bible-believing Christians. And, if questioned in private, one or two will insist they were approached in a dream by a man who was white and looked just like the Norwegian Jesus with whom we are all familiar, and told to run for the presidency because it was God-ordained and America was desperately in need of their leadership.

Together, they were a pod of indistinguishable and unqualified white men, at least one token white businesswoman, and a seemingly disoriented black man, both the white woman and the black guy there for ballast and sleight-of-hand, because this is the modern Republican Party. All of them were as incoherent in their reasons for wanting to be president as Jeffery Dahmer was in trying to explain why he really enjoyed eating the people he murdered. They gathered before journalists who asked questions that were meaningless at best, questions supposedly designed to "test the candidates' mettle." But this Republican Primary, this 2016 creep show, unlike any before, had morphed into a dangerous circus filled with insane clowns and rabid animals.

I had been slowly recovering from the shock of living through eight years of global chaos caused by the warped bastards who orchestrated the George W. Bush Follies, or more correctly, "Adventures In Multiple War Crimes," and then, after the International Criminal Court decided not to issue arrest warrants for those killers, came eight years of the Presidency of Professor Cool, Barack Obama. He promised hope and change to a country in desperate need of an exorcism. It didn't work. The Klan sympathizers, neo-Fascists, and Congressional Republicans, led by the execrable Mitch McConnell, verbally attacked and slashed President Cool every time he suggested that working together honestly and openly might make for a better outcome than the daily demonstrations of lies and stupidity that are the hallmarks of Republican governance. Diogenes, in his fruitless search, would have given up, gone home, and pulled the covers over his head after he saw the Republican reaction to Obama's election, much less his 8-year-long attempt to find something, *anything*, that might convince the Republicans to conduct themselves like adults and focus on managing the country instead of behaving like maniacal 10-year-olds armed with machetes and hell-bent on its dismemberment.

While the political wreckage was building, I found myself at the absolute limit of my tolerance for any more of the bullshit. After thirty-five years working in radio and, in that capacity, trying through dialogue with my listeners to find a few shreds of coherence of purpose from the so-called "leadership class," I knew the grand experiment in self-governance had run its course and a more subtle fascism (no invasions, no death camps; at least not right away) was about to take the stage in the bloated persona of Donald Trump.

I'd been hooked up – like a chemo infusion - to either MSNBC or CNN for weeks, months, all of 2016. A terrible admission, but every day staring in disbelief at the television, turning to Politifact to cross-check the more insane statements coming from the stupidest, least coherent, most uneducated liar ever to decide to run for president. The fact that he was a serial adulterer and sexual predator was an apparent added bonus for the Christian leaders who enthusiastically endorsed him and the fools who voted for him. He produced an endless loop of incoherent gibberish which, if listened to long enough, was like being pushed to the edge of a dark, cold, abyss filled with clicking scorpions and poisonous snakes. Unless, of course, you bought into the bullshit being peddled by that string of Christian enablers who see Trump as a short-cut to theocracy. With no sense of irony whatsoever, these "Christians" who have warned against the anti-Christ for millennia, embrace him and make him their leader when he finally arrives.

So, I reached the point if I had one more instance of seeing Trump's bloated orange face, hair swept up on the sides to meet at the back of his head in that duck's-ass style all the wannabe Blackboard Jungle-type high-school punks sported in the 1950s, or any more of those weird *il Duce* poses that surely had been rehearsed in front of a gold-trimmed full-length mirror, I was afraid I'd conclude the end of civilization truly was at hand and it was time to arm up and head for the mountains. But there was no possibility of escaping from the horror of it all. I couldn't pull the plug and ignore this orange Oompa Loompa. Ever since the slow escalator ride down from somewhere inaccessible to normal people, and the declaration that he was going to run for President of The United States in order to stop the invasion of women and babies from the Hell-gate recently opened in Mexico, I had been transfixed. Is this really happening?

The knee-slapping guffaws that ricocheted coast-to-coast, border-to-border, across the fruited plane that a fake self-declared billionaire, third-rate television reality "star" with the measurable brain power of road-kill thought he had a chance at becoming . . . *The Leader Of The Free World?!* began immediately after his descent from the clouds in the upper reaches of Trump Tower. That's some funny shit, right?

Of course, that occurred before the bowel-churning realization that somehow this country had forgotten or decided to ignore or were simply ignorant of the warnings found in Sinclair Lewis' 1935 novel "It Can't Happen Here," or Philip Roth's "The Plot Against America," or the cold madness of Orwell's "1984". Despite the warnings in all those predictive novels, Trump was still attracting crowds of belligerent white people who looked and sounded like they'd just come from a massive rat-killing: A little glassy-eyed, flushed, screaming shit like "Lock Her Up!" or "Build The Wall!" and showing the sort of release that usually comes only during a Baptist Revival tent meeting. Or a public hanging. Or the Two Minutes of Hate.

Watching all this, I realized we were sliding into a state of carefully engineered political chaos; that honest-to-god Fascism had arrived in the persona of a 70-year-old world-class grifter and his soulless family. Worse, a creepy following of strange looking and stranger sounding cretins began to show up, clustering around Trump in anticipation of riding this wave of madness into the White House, a collection of con-artists Trump insisted were "the best people ever." All at once the meme on those goofy-ass red baseball hats looked more like a warning than a slogan.

And then . . . seventeen months later . . . *No!* This slow-walking empty suit, he with the crimson tie so violently red it appeared one of his carotids had been sliced open, and the language of an aging Mafia don, was declared President of The United States!! And, there, on the victory stage at his political headquarters were his family and their multiple retainers grinning and looking and sounding like the Beverly Hillbillies meet the Romanovs.

There is no mystery, no confusion, as to how we arrived at this destructive melding of the absolute worst of American Capitalism and European Fascism. Every time I hear someone whine, "How did this happen? How did Donald Trump get elected president? Is God this pissed off at us? Is the world ending?" I feel compelled to point out we did it to ourselves – which always evokes a blank look or an insistence that I'm full of shit and possibly an America-hating Communist.

But, we did. With our eyes wide shut.

How did we get to yet another moment of Fascism after millions of people were obliterated before it was caged the last time the world had to endure its singular spasm of totalitarianism? How did the US hit a point so low that enough of us – especially the Christian lunatics - decided to choose as President a willfully ignorant, un-read, pussy-grabbing, white nationalist, fear-mongering, dictator-wannabe to lead us into a truly insane and, given the real and frightening possibility of human extinction, possibly short future; a man who had turned mediocrity into not just an art form, but also into a snarling beast? And, most important, is there a path back to reality from this nightmare? Is there a way to revisit 2016 and shove it into a Ministry of Truth memory hole where it will disappear, irretrievable, forever? Where's Winston Smith when he's really needed?

I finally realized there was only one thing left to do in order to clean this monster out of my head: write a book. About Trump? That was the original idea. Put all the rage I was feeling into writing. Purge. But, I quickly realized I couldn't. The anger I felt from what I was witnessing was too extreme and every time I sat in front of the keyboard my mind went blank.

So, I decided instead to write a memoir in an attempt to divert myself from the craziness that was flooding the country. I would write about some often fun and often weird and unexplainable events that I've experienced. This was to be my therapy, a way to ignore the Orange Monster, if only while writing.

This, then, is the result.

Acknowledgement

This project was made possible by the combined financial generosity of a number of people who have been listeners to my radio program, and now podcast, for periods of time ranging from decades to months. Through the Kickstarter crowd-funding site, we received the support we asked for and more. For that support I am absolutely grateful. The following are the names of those whose faith in what I was doing made it a reality. Thank you.

Rod Stasick, Angela Davie, Andrew Bosworth, Cynthia Baye, John Farrell, Craig S. Snyder, Zemula Fleming, Tomas Herazo, Brian Wolman, Colleen Sandie, Jude Morford, Leonardo Calderon, Michael, Robert Cohen, Zenda Boss-Hall, Francis Leckie, James Miller, Hernan Schulein, Scott Sandvik, Bill Coleman, Eric Sieverling, Regina Avraham, Vincent Maron, Rocky Van Asten, Johnathan Thompson, Kurt J. Keiser, Kimberley Peterson, Mark O Dochartaigh, Steve, Robert Reynolds, Chad Slack, Toni Shorthouse, Nancy Rose-Balamut, Fran Merriman, Lynn, Charles Denison, Frederik Vorderhake, Ed Engelmann, Royeh, David Mendriski, Dee Dee Thompson, Timucua, William Wallace, Albert Caldarelli, Jeff Hartke, Joe Earley, Lisa Selvidge, Cynthia Leeder, Emily Covington, Craig Wruck, John Pritchard, Sharon Baughman, Preston Rogers, Joni Ellsworth, Ron Sadowski, Charles A. Hoefel, John W. White

III, Jennifer Mason, Kathleen MacColl, Chuck J, Scott D. Unruh, Marcus Sterling, Sanche Llewellyn, Michael C. Donow, Steven Penn, Robert McQuaid, Thomas Foerster, Robert Wilmers, Stephanie Weber, Ski Anderson, Jon in Maryland, Les Meyers, Shirley Johnson, and Janet K. Scapin.

Chapter 1

The N Word

Toward the end of World War II, a few humid August days before president Truman gave the order to annihilate two cities in Japan and in the process incinerate the 200-thousand-plus men, women and children who lived in Hiroshima and Nagasaki, my mother, Silvia, found a small one-bedroom apartment in Toledo, Ohio, that had once been an attic, and moved the two of us in. Just the two of us. (My father didn't enter my life until later.) Housing during and immediately after the war was nearly nonexistent. Any available space, even one that had been converted from an attic, was a lucky find for working class people, certainly for a single mother, unwed, who arrived with a toddler, two cardboard suitcases and a bulging diaper bag.

It was a three-story, outside walk-up with terrible ventilation; impossibly hot in the summer, cold and damp in the winter. At one end of this redesigned, L-shaped attic was a bedroom; at the other, a kitchen with a bathroom near the single door that led in and out. In winter the only warmth was from a small gas space heater situated half-way down a very short hall that became our living room. If, at night, the heater's pilot light were to go out, the gas would slowly fill the tiny apartment until the entire house exploded jolting the neighbors awake in terror, convinced the Japs had finally found a way to drop incendiary devices into America's heartland. It was to be my home for the next fourteen years along with – eventually – my father, two brothers, a sister, and a small dog, six of us in a space no bigger than 300 square feet. The thought of that pilot light going out haunted me nightly, especially after my grandmother taught me the creepy children's prayer, *Now I lay me down to sleep, I pray the Lord my soul to keep, if I should die before I wake. . .* I wondered if the little kids in Hiroshima had recited a Japanese version of that prayer the night before they were changed from elementary school children into airborne pieces of particulate matter that mingled with the dust of what had been, an instant before, buildings, automobiles, houses, flowers, grasses, and dreams.

By age ten I had a paper route. Early each morning, hours before school started, I went down the outside three flights of stairs to the front porch where a bundle of newspapers had been dropped off. I read the headlines as I folded them for delivery and most of what I read scared the hell out of me. The world beyond Toledo was crazed and violent: A killer fog in London had suffocated thousands; the number of American dead in the Korean war was mounting; there was talk of once again using nuclear weapons against an Asian enemy; the *Mau Mau* rebellion in Kenya had started and the killings there were enough to give a ten-year-old white boy the night terrors, especially if he had seen all those Tarzan movies with the screaming natives covered in huge white feathers, shrunken heads tied and bouncing crazily around their waists, running after terrified blond women who were trying to sprint through the jungle in *bwana* dresses and high heels.

On and on they went; newspaper articles that were dark and filled with horror story after horror story. And then in the winter of 1953, the scariest man on earth, Joseph Stalin, died. There it was, his photo, on the front page of the *Toledo Times.* Thanks to the steady flow of anti-Communist stories of torture and enslavement in the atheistic Soviet Union, we fifth-graders knew who Stalin was. Because of him, the Pledge of Allegiance was about to be changed to include an American god. I knew I was supposed to feel relieved about his death. I didn't, though, maybe because the news photos of his waxy corpse lying in state, colorless flowers stacked around him, uniformed Communists frozen in black and white as they marched past the funeral bier as if in a trance, was all too goddam weird to bring about a feeling of relief.

Every morning brought news of another blast of bloody death from somewhere in the world. It was a graduate level course in how violent the world really was. For a now-11-year-old it was difficult to comprehend and not at all like the friendly stories in my monthly copies of *Boys Life* magazine. How could there be such a difference between the two worlds? There was insanity at home, too. Not just in my attic, where every day raised the possibility of some sort of trauma, but in the entire country. The times were changing fast. There was a massive post-war migration of black families flowing out of the South, each one searching for a place that was not filled with terror and violence and poverty, fleeing the South for the same reasons my maternal grandparents left Italy in the first decade of the 20th century: to find in the New World a life that could be lived. Laws were being passed to end

Jim Crow in the old Confederacy, to grant black citizens the right to vote without fear of being lynched for the attempt, to provide equal opportunity where it concerned education, jobs, and housing, laws that were unenforced and ignored, as millions of Southern whites, in cities and towns scattered across the Old Confederacy, found all the changes they could not accept, coming too quickly. In response to these laws, the incidences of lynchings, beatings, and night-rider terror increased exponentially.

In Toledo, as much as in any other northern city, the changing complexion of the neighborhoods and schools and factories pushed race relations to the forefront of most adult conversations. It was a subject laced with fear and ignorance. During the commercials that interrupted the weekend radio broadcasts of the Cleveland Indians, the men sitting in folding lawn chairs in their driveways or on their porches, dressed in sleeve-less undershirts and drinking bottle after bottle of cheap Buckeye Beer, would bring up yet again the argument about whether Jackie Robinson was as good as the white players and how long it would be before others like him flooded the major leagues, and why did the Dodgers hire a colored player to begin with?

As we got older, black kids and white kids in the neighborhood played together, usually either football in a vacant lot, or pick-up baseball in a grocery store parking area, trying to ignore the attitudes of the adults around us, including our parents. But the divisions of race had been deeply buried inside all of us, black kids as well as white kids. Our playing together didn't change the day-to-day reality of white superiority or white privilege, terms we had never heard, and neither concept was even considered because it all seemed to fit the natural order of things. When the game was over we all went home, back to our respective racial worlds. It was an especially weird feeling for me, all the adult talk of this white superiority, because the black kids lived in duplexes or actual houses and I lived in an attic. So, where was the privilege, much less the superiority, in living in an attic? The first time I spoke to a dark-skinned man I said what I thought was friendly and proper. I was in kindergarten, five years old and already aware that a colored person was not treated the same as a white person. I didn't know why.

"Hi, Nigger!" I smiled. The man I just insulted was inside the potato chip factory that stood adjacent to our house, washing the windows that opened onto the small backyard where I was playing. He looked up, stared at me for a moment, but said nothing. I still remember the look in his eyes as he stood there absorbing the deep insult from a smiling little shit of a five-year-old white boy. Silvia was hanging wet laundry on the clothes-line a few feet away and heard what I said. She called me to her side and whispered that decent people never use that word. Had I been seven or eight instead of five going on six I would have called bullshit because it was a word spoken casually by most of the adult white people I knew, even in my own family.

"It's a bad word, Michael."

"But, I've heard Daddy use it," I said.

"Well, he shouldn't. Now, I want you to go back over to that man and tell him you're sorry."

"Why, Mom?"

"Because the proper word is *colored*; he is a colored man, not the word you used."

"Do, I say, 'I'm sorry 'colored man'?"

"No! Just say you're sorry. You don't have to say 'colored.'"

I was getting confused. In my kindergarten class, we had white Crayons and lots of colored Crayons and the colored ones were all different colors. When we asked for a colored one, we had to name the color: red? blue? yellow?

"Do I say I'm sorry brown man? Because he is brown, Mom."

She dropped the clothes-pins into the basket at her feet and looked down at me with that look Italian mothers use when they are mere seconds from whacking your ass with whatever's close enough to use as an ass-whacker. I knew that look and knew it was time to do what I was being told.

"No! Just say you're sorry. Go do it. Now!"

I walked back to the factory window where he was still working. "I'm sorry I said that, mister. . . um . . . mister . . ." I didn't have a word for him except "Nigger." Or "colored." So, I just stood there. He looked at me and once again said nothing. Then, after wiping the dirt from a few more window panes he picked up the bucket of dirty wash water, turned his back and walked away, into the factory's deep shadows.

Chapter 2

Breaking Away

In 1959, when I was ready to begin my senior year in High School, two days before the term was to begin, I left home, this time for good. I had done this before, several times, after my mother had bailed out of the family attic and left her abusive common-law husband three years earlier. Joe, my Irish, fallen-Catholic father, infused all our lives with a constant flow of violence, the worst directed to my mother who finally realized she had to leave or be killed. Joe suffered from his submerged Catholicism in the worst way: monumental guilt he was unable to manage or resolve. Catholics invented guilt and an elaborate system to expiate it or magnify its consequences. And since it was their invention, they developed exquisite ways to use it to inflict hideous pain that would follow an apostate Catholic beyond death and into the violent after-world they had constructed. First, Purgatory and then on into Hell unless enough punishment had been applied and the sinner was now scourged and clean. Then, possibly, maybe, the Catholic heaven. There was no redemption without confession and punishment. You could stand before the Holy

Mother and scream for release from your sins, shriek Novenas, pray Acts of Contrition until your lips dissolved. All to no avail. Your ass was doomed. At least that's how my old man perceived the fate that was waiting for him because he knew he had violated a foundational Catholic belief. By abandoning his first marriage he had committed adultery, and, therefore a mortal sin. Worse, he had begun years before to question the superstitious bullshit that saturated his religion, which, in turn, gave rise to the guilt and the fear. They would always be there, like a bubble of acid eating through his stomach. World without end, amen. The combination made him violent, abusive, destructive.

When he was sixteen his Irish parents (Grandparents I never knew) sent him to a Jesuit school in Connecticut for three years to study for the priesthood. His brother, my uncle Jack, was to be a cop. That's how it works in a conservative Catholic family that produces two sons. (Thank you, Holy Mother!) One to be a priest, one to be a cop. However, Joe realized being a priest was just not the direction in which he wanted to go. The studies were difficult and saturated with hard-core Catholic history. He was an excellent student – math and Vulgate Latin were his strongest subjects. But, seminary students, especially once they became priests, could never have sex – unless, maybe, occasionally, with an altar boy who knew to do exactly as instructed by Father Molester or hell's open gates awaited. Joe, however, like most heterosexual teen-age boys wanted sex with girls. There was no chance of that happening given the circumstances he faced for the next seven years at seminary. He couldn't have sex, unless it was with one of the staff priests. Joe wanted sex with women. So, for that compelling reason and others more profound and ambitious, good-bye seminary.

The calling to serve the Christian god simply was not there. The Jesuits found that unacceptable. He left the seminary, anyway, Jesuit threats be damned, and completed his formal education at a secular college where sex was available. But, having been forced to worship a vengeful god in the first place, the time came when the same god ambushed him in the most painful way. It was a violent ambush.

It happened like this: His first marriage was to a Catholic woman named Yvonne. They had two children, a boy, Jack, and a girl, Patty. Joe, apparently, was an ideal and conscientious father. He took good care of his family, but Patty was his favorite. One summer day, when she was four years old, Joe took her swimming in the Blanchard River, a shallow waterway that flowed through the middle of Findlay, Ohio. Joe watched her closely as she splashed and waded and ducked under the water near the riverbank, surfacing with a mouthful of water, spraying it into the air like a cherub in a Roman fountain. When Patty was sufficiently tired from all the activity, she fell asleep on Joe's lap and snuggled close for her afternoon nap.

Later that evening, when everyone was ready for bed, Patty complained of severe stomach pain. Joe sat with her as the night wore on and the symptoms worsened. First, projectile vomiting, followed by bloody diarrhea. Then a fever and clammy skin. Yvonne called for the doctor who arrived as quickly as he could. After examining her the doctor gave Joe and Yvonne the unacceptable verdict: Cholera. Joe held her close for the next few days. He bathed her in cool tap water, trying to reduce her fever. A little past three o'clock on the fifth day of her sickness, she asked, "Daddy, can I have an ice cream?" She then closed her eyes and died.

It was too much for Joe. His grief was overwhelming. And,

9

he knew why Patty had been taken. It had to be his god at work, a merciless phantom who dealt severely with those who would leave the faith, especially those who had been delivered to be a priest. There was simply no other explanation that made sense to Joe. His inculcation into the blood cult that is Christianity was impossible to refute. *Vengeance is mine, saith the Lord.* Eventually, the guilt took over his ability to function at all. And there was more than just his daughter's death. Hadn't his mother taken in other families' stinking laundry to earn money for his schooling? Hadn't she prayed daily, kneeling in humility before a statue of the Holy Mother in the sanctuary of Saint Joseph's church – the very church whose name he carried? You can't do shit like that to your dear Catholic Mother and escape the blast furnace of guilt. Not with the Blessed Virgin weeping and a crowd of Saints watching and moaning like beasts from hell.

Because of this religious torture Joe sank into an almost comatose state of depression shortly after he fathered his second set of children, of which I was the oldest. His second wife, Silvia, told us his story as a way of trying to explain the frequent violence. For years, the only time we kids saw him was when he stumbled from the bedroom shouting that since we had neither been baptized nor confirmed in the Church we were as doomed to Hell as he was. Then off came his belt and the beatings commenced. There was no escape. Until, finally, there was.

It became a driving force; to get away from this nightmare life as soon as I was old enough and before one of us was killed, Joe or me. On a stifling summer afternoon, a few days after my 17th birthday and two months before school was to begin, I packed a couple of grocery bags with clothing, books, toothbrush and anything else I felt was necessary for immediate survival, said a teary good-bye to my brothers and sister, and fled. Eventually, one by one, as they grew older, so did they.

Twenty-five years later, submerged deep in the roiling madness of paranoid schizophrenia, Joe died, alone, in a nursing home shouting incoherently at the demons waiting for him in a Christian hell not of his making, waiting to administer the punishment that his religion demanded.

Chapter 3

Lipstick Lesbians

Living alone in a one-room apartment at age seventeen in 1959 had a certain cachet, for sure, even though most of it was not so good. Completing my senior year was a necessity. If I didn't graduate and go on to college, I'd wind up working in one of the city's factories producing auto parts for the next 30 years just like most of the male population of Toledo. Fuck that.

Two years earlier, the year I turned 15, when Joe's mental anguish made it impossible for him to work, impossible most days to get him out of bed, I had to find a way to make more money than I made delivering papers. My brothers and sisters and I needed things, things like food, clothing, bus fare, school supplies, Scout dues, hand soap, shampoo, toilet paper. In a near panic I answered a help wanted ad that promised I could earn a lot of money simply by talking to people, asking them survey questions. An interview would decide if I had the qualifications, the personality, the *chutzpah*. When I arrived at the interview address, a hotel room in downtown Toledo, the hallway was wall-to-wall boys, some with a parent in tow, most of us alone, all of us white. We were told to enter the interview room five at a time. Once inside we were questioned by two men who smiled a lot. Yes, they said, you boys will be asking survey questions. We were to go door-to-door, in the early evening after school, while the men waited for us at the end of the block. Then on to the next street. And then the next.

The questions we were to ask were about magazines; the whole thing was about magazines. Survey questions, my ass. We were going to sell subscriptions. Door to door. In truth, it was a good after school job. A lot of walking, meeting complete strangers and learning how to start and hold a conversation. The goal was to sell magazines, but the experience of learning to take care of myself would be invaluable, the interviewers promised. So, I worked on developing a winning persona, one that would make the lady of the house open the door to this smiling lad standing on her front porch, a facade that was total bullshit because the truth was I quickly came to despise the people who opened their doors, these people who lived in nice brick ranch houses, in their immaculate subdivisions, with the fragrance of a carefully prepared home-cooked supper flooding over me with each door that opened. And, always, the slight look of pity with which each person said, "Yes? May I help you, young man?" I despised them because I knew they had what I thought I would never have and the pain of that was almost unbearable. I felt as though I lived on a different planet, in a different reality. Sometimes, when I reached the end of one of the streets I was supposed to canvas, I found a place where I wouldn't be seen, under a tree, behind a gas station, and wept burning tears of envy, fear, jealousy. But I was learning to take care of myself.

After a couple of years of this, the repetition of it all was becoming excruciatingly boring. And, walking door-to-door in the deep-freeze that are Ohio winters was a good way to lose a couple of toes to frostbite and gangrene. One cold, slush-saturated late afternoon with my best high school friend and co-magazine seller, Jerry Stiles, we decided it was time to split, time for a road trip South where it was warm, where we heard the air was filled with the fragrance of orange trees and hibiscus bushes, not the acrid stench of industrial chemicals and the eye-stinging smog that was slowly eating away our lung tissue. Jerry's great-aunt lived in Clearwater, Florida. I could taste the oranges.

Jerry was one of the few students at Scott High – he may have been the only one - who was genuinely envious of the life I was living.

"Your own apartment? Man! Talk about being able to do what you want! No one bitching at you. Nobody telling you to do this, do that. Chicks any time you want. You are so lucky!" He saw my situation as one of total freedom, the sort every teenage boy desperately wants. He had no idea of the downside; no one to talk with, no one to wake you up in the morning or say goodnight when you went to bed, no one to have dinner with, no one to help you make decisions in situations about which you had no understanding, no frame of reference. He lived with his divorced mother and sister and hadn't had the influence or discipline of his father since his parents split when he was eight years old. His study habits were nonexistent, his grades were barely passing, but, he knew how to raise hell and, after seeing the film with the same name had adopted the persona of a true rebel without a cause, although in Jerry's case it was more rebel without a clue. He was tall and carried his height with a definite swagger that said he took no bullshit from anybody, which was incredibly ironic because he was a virtual fountain of bullshit. He had been picked up by the police twice, once for stealing candy bars at a super market check-out, and once for vandalism after he threw rocks through every window in a house that was obviously empty and up for sale. Each time, his mother went to the police station and, after pleading with officers who had him in custody, got him released without going through the courts and the subsequent permanence of an arrest record.

He, like me, was constantly looking to get laid, only in a much more open and blatant way, an unending quest that often resulted in unexpected success. We both had fake IDs that got us into the local dance clubs and beer joints on Saturday nights where we cruised for the girls who came to Toledo from nearby Detroit. There was no "low beer" law in Michigan. You had to be twenty-one just to enter a bar, which meant the hell-raising party girls made the forty-five-mile drive south where the weekends could dissolve into a haze of drinking and unprotected sex. Once inside a favorite club, and as long as we didn't try to order an actual mixed drink and stuck with the low-alcohol beer or a cola, we were ignored by the bartenders and waitresses. Jerry quickly realized that by bringing his own booze into the clubs, usually a pint of whiskey he hid in his jacket pocket, he could, by adding a quick pour into his glass of Coke, avoid that ridiculous requirement of paying for drinks. Of course, his soft drink eventually became a glass of pure booze. At age seventeen, he was well on his way to a lifetime of AA meetings, if not a long stretch in prison for some alcohol-related crime. Or, maybe, an early death. But, he was my best friend and therefore his larceny and occasionally crazed behavior was simply part of his charm.

One humid Saturday night, during our summer vacation, we decided to go to a club in downtown Toledo, the Ivanhoe, that was notorious for its clientele: gay people; lesbians and homosexual men. A friend assured us the place attracted "lip-stick lesbians," young women who didn't sport the butch look but who got dressed to kill on Saturday nights – short shorts, skintight skirts and body-hugging dresses, four-inch stiletto heels, big hair and heavy on the make-up; the best fantasy goddesses imaginable for teen-age boys - and were looking for excitement. And, if that meant getting it on with another woman because the men were boring assholes, well, let's rock and roll. And this was where Jerry and I would come to the rescue. We knew these lovely lesbians were lesbian only because they hadn't had a night filled with the erotic madness of men who knew how to properly handle the girls' sexual urges, and thus had to turn to women who did know. Jerry and I were absolutely convinced we were the men who could open those doors to sexual satisfaction. We would lift these misguided women up from their lesbian misery into the joy of man-woman sex. It was our mission. Any tangential sexual pleasure we might experience was absolutely beside the point, we insisted to each other.

When we arrived, the Ivanhoe was packed. We pushed through the clot of bodies that crowded the entrance and into the club. Tables and booths surrounded a large dance floor and, along one side a bar stretched the length of the room. The jukebox had several speakers scattered about and the music – Broadway show tunes and dance numbers – pounded into the frenzied crowd. There were bodies everywhere. The air was thick with sweat and seduction. A foursome was leaving, and we quickly claimed the booth they had been sitting in. We ordered Seven-and-Sevens and somehow got away with it. Our waitress (waiter?) slapped two drink napkins and a paper bowl of heavily salted popcorn on the table and faded into the pulsating dance crowd.

"Holy shit!" Jerry shouted above the music and screaming that filled the club. "Is this a mind-fuck or what? Lookit the queers! Look! Those guys are dancing, for god's sake! And, he's got his hand on the other guy's ass! *Jesus!* And, check out the honeys! Look at the one with the long black hair! *Holy shit!* Hey! Those two chicks are kissing!" I thought Jerry was close to a stroke, if for no other reason than his head snapping around from left to right, back to left, *snap!* right, *snap*, left. I had to tell him twice to stop fucking pointing at people. "You wanna get thrown out? Quit acting like we just got off a hay wagon!"

It was crazy. Men with men, women with women, touching and kissing and groping each other openly and laughing and drinking and dancing and it was difficult realizing the people having such a blast were considered freaks, sinners, twisted perverts, law-breakers, tempters of children, and were all going to burn in hell forever and ever, world without end, amen and amen. So, there they were, there it was. All the crap and lies we'd been taught was right in front of us dancing their asses off. And, Jerry and I were gonna be part of it. The not gay part, of course.

Two girls were sitting at a table near us. A moment before they had been on the dance floor grinding their hips together to the slow, jazzy beat of Nina Simone's *I Loves You, Porgy*. The short dark-haired one was wearing pale yellow pedal-pushers and a white blouse with the ubiquitous Peter Pan collar. The taller one a black turtle neck sweater and the shortest shorts

17

we had ever seen. The slight curve of her ass cheeks peeked out from the edge of the cuffs. Jerry and I glanced at each other. "You go first," he said. "I get the blond. No tits, but I like tall chicks. You can have the one with the Audrey Hepburn haircut." I wasn't about to argue. They were both cute and smiled at us as we decided who would make the first move. I pushed through the crowd to their table.

"Hi, my name's Mike. You girls having fun?" What a stupid opening line. I stood there waiting for an invitation to sit or get lost.

Giggling. "Fun?" the pixie haircut asked. "Oh, yeah, we're definitely having fun, right Sybil?"

"We sure are. How about you . . . Mike? Are you having fun, too?"

"Um, not yet. We just got here." More stupid.

So, that was the blond's name, Sybil, Jerry's girl. Pixie-cut smiled at me and the black light that flooded the club made her smile dazzling. "My name's Bobbie Jo but my friends just call me BJ." Jerry materialized. "Hey, ladies!" he shouted above the music. "I'm Jerry. My friend Mikey and I come here all the time. Never seen you two honeys before." My true to form friend let loose with the night's

first load of bullshit.

I asked Bobbie Jo to dance. Before I finished the question, she was on the dance floor, twisting and sliding through the constantly moving crowd, her hand outstretched toward me. She mouthed, *c'mon! c'mon!* BJ could dance, if the moves she was making could be called that. I had never seen a girl move so seductively, so freely, as if there were no one to stop her and why would they want to? I took her hand and was pulled instantly into her body. On the jukebox, a slow song;

Nina was again singing, "*. . . don't let him take me, don't let him handle me with his hot hands . . .*" as though that was the only slow record the club allowed, and it was to be played over and over whenever the music wasn't bone-vibrating rock and roll. Each time Simone sang those two lines, the crowd joined in, some of the couples whispering the words, others blaring them into the smoke and the sweat and the lust, as though challenging their partner. I found myself positively drowning in this sex-charged, pulsating place. The flickering lights, the low rumble of sounds from the crowd, the thickening music, and the weirdness of dancing so close to a stranger, a girl I had just met, as close as familiar lovers. I realized I was clinging to BJ, not holding her, more than a little light-headed from a couple of Seven-Sevens and what must have been a very low oxygen count in the room. "You wanna sit down?" she asked. "You're looking sorta flustered. You don't come here often, you and your friend, do you." It was a statement, not a question. "Well . . . actually . . . no," I answered. "No, um, this is our first time here. It's really cool." *Cool?*

Jerry and Sybil materialized out of the smoke, like two floating spirits. Jerry was drunk and enjoying the hell out of being with Sybil, which was obvious by the way he was stroking her barely covered ass. "Heyyyyyyyy, Mikey! Is this what's happening, or what? I love this place!" His free arm swept the room behind him. "I fucking love it!" Within seconds they were again absorbed by the crowd, Jerry's exuberant shouts fading into the smoke and music.

BJ said she wanted to sit for a moment, freshen her drink. We tried talking over the pounding noise, shouting at each other when the volume reached ear-splitting.

"Are you in school?" I asked, trying to disguise the real

reason Jerry were in the club, trying to be conversational.

"Not during the summer, silly. It's play time, right? And, I graduated last year, anyway."

"Oh . . . yeah . . . of course. What about later, you know, the Fall?"

"Then, it's on to the city, New York! I'm going to be a designer, Mikey. I have so many ideas for exciting women's clothing, so many outrageous ways to make a woman look like more than the painted drudges who prance around their kitchens in dresses and high heels, making casseroles for hubby and the kids. You see them every night on television, don't you? Isn't that disgusting? I just want to change all that, you know? I know I can do it. I know I can."

Harriet Nelson, Ricky's mom, disgusting? *Leave it to Beaver's* mom? And the women who sold us Chevrolets and Frigidaire refrigerators? I never thought of them as disgusting. They were just real. Although, I didn't know any and none of my friends had moms who looked like the ones on television. Still, did BJ really find them disgusting?

"Well . . ." I started to answer.

"They make me crazy, Mikey! I want women to be daring and flamboyant and exciting in the way they dress! Why shouldn't they?"

I didn't answer. I had never considered Moms to be anything other than, well, Moms. BJ leaned closer to me. "What's your last name, handsome? You afraid to tell me? Gotta be more there than just Mikey."

I told her my last name. She thought for a moment and then clapped her hands together in delight. "Well, then, I'll call you 'M and M.' Like the candy! *'Melts in your mouth and not in your hand!'*" she laughed out the advertising slogan. "I'll bet you'd do that M and M, right?" The music slowed. "C'mon, M and M, let's dance!"

We crowded on to the dance floor again, and this time when Nina got to the . . ."*don't let him handle me with his hot hands. . .*" part I slid one hand up BJ's back and cradled her pixie-ish head against my shoulder. I felt her sigh and fold into me. Her left ear was close to my mouth, so I blew into it. We knew that blowing into a girl's ear made them wild with uncontrollable passion. BJ just tightened the death-grip hold she already had around my waist. It felt like she was trying to slide into my body, which was a lot different from dancing with my female classmates at the high school sock hops. I nibbled the edge of her ear. She started squirming, twisting from side to side. I could feel the heat flowing to my groin. I stuck the tip of my tongue into her ear, just the tip. She moaned. I could feel it rather than hear it. The noise was deafening. I slid my hand slowly down her back, feeling the soft cottony fabric give way as I went lower and lower. Then she started to get an erection.

Poor little lesbian, I thought. So desperate to maintain her disguise she's put something in her pedal pushers, maybe a little banana. But the little banana kept getting bigger, pushing into my upper thigh. And then, way too late, the truth slid home.

". . . *don't let him handle me with his hot hands . . .*" I stopped dancing and pushed BJ back, so I could see her face. "What is *that*?" I asked, glancing toward her now clearly defined crotch, very concerned what the answer would be.

"What do you think it is, Mikey? M and M. My curious dance partner. Can you guess?"

"C'mon, no bullshit. Is that a . . . *dick?!* Do you have a dick?" Lost and confused.

21

"Well, honey, the way you were nibbling my ear, how do you expect a girl to react? You wanna do that some more?"

"Okay, seriously, BJ, are you a boy or a girl?"

"I thought you knew."

"Yeah, well, I thought you were a girl!"

"Well, I sorta am, Mikey."

"What does that mean? You can't be 'sorta' something. You're either one or the other. C'mon, what were you when the doctor slapped you on the ass when you were born?"

"Well, if you want to go back *that* far, okay, I was a very cute little baby boy. With complications. Sort of. But, Mikey, that was a long time ago, honey. Right now, I'm just a girl enjoying dancing. With you. Is there a problem with that?"

Damn. I was trying to understand what she was telling me, and it wasn't working. She was BJ, this cute girl I had met a few hours ago in this gay bar who was trying to sort out her sexuality. And, I was there to help her, so to speak. That's all. Or, was she a cute boy who was simply on the make and I was the target?

I saw Jerry pushing through the crowd toward us, Sybil following him with a look that did not say, *"wheeee, we're having funnnnn . . ."*

He shouted, "Hey, guess what my man? Guess who I've been dancing with?" He turned to Sybil. "I've been dancing with . . . her. But, she's not a her. She's a him. A guy! She's got a *cock!*" Several nearby dancers looked in our direction and grinned. "Lucky you!" one shouted above the pounding music.

We decided to get out of the way of the thumping crowd of dancers and sit down, have a drink, and sort out who was who and what was what, which was suddenly extremely difficult – no, impossible - for Jerry and me. We came into this bar thinking we'd convert a couple of mis-guided lesbians back into the natural order of things where men were men – even young ones like us – and women were grateful. Fat fucking chance of *that* happening. We were the tricksters who had been tricked. The four of us managed to avoid the hysteria Jerry and I were feeling and talked about the absurdity of two young stud wannabes – Jerry and me – venturing into a place where the rules not only didn't apply, they didn't exist. Not the rules we were familiar with. The heterosexual rules. Not here. Not with Nina Simone singing her anthem to pure lust.

"You boys should have known what you were doing," Sybil said as she drew circles in the melt from her drink glass. "In the first place, don't you think it was kind of arrogant? You were going to walk into a place totally unknown to you and start changing people? Wow! That's some balls, guys, really. And, it could also get you into a situation you couldn't have handled."

BJ was looking at me, her eyes dark in the smoky club. She wanted to tell me something beyond the lecture she was delivering to two lost boys. I could feel it. I still could not see her as a guy, even after the surprise erection. She wasn't a boy with complications. She was a girl with complications. Jerry and I got up to leave; we had to after being chastised for the shitty thing we had tried to do. BJ reached up and took my hand and brought it to her lips. "Bye, Mikey," she said. "I sure wish things were a bit different . . ." In that moment, so did I.

We walked out to the parking lot and got into Jerry's car. He lit a cigarette and we both sat quietly, neither of us daring to say a word about what had just happened. Finally, "Well, that was a mind-fuck," he said. "Let's get outta here. That place was a drag, anyway."

We drove away. I wonder if BJ ever made it to New York. I wonder if she ever designed the clothing that lifted women from drudgery to her promise of excitement! Flamboyance! Beauty! I hope she did.

Chapter 4

Going South

We made the decision to leave Toledo one dark, cold January Saturday late in the afternoon while we were slogging through icy black slush after two hours of no one opening their doors to listen to our magazine pitch. We heard the same shout, or something similar, coming from inside each of the warm, snug-looking, houses:

"We don't want any!"

"But we have a couple of survey questions. It'll just take a minute! Please?"

"Go the fuck away before I call the cops! Get off my goddam porch!"

"Well, fuck you, too! Asshole." Thus, I was learning to take care of myself.

The skies were leaden and low, heavy with piercing needles of soot and black ice crystals. The temperature hovered near whatever was below death by freezing. We stopped at a convenience store and cashed the paychecks we had been handed earlier that afternoon. Together they totaled just under one hundred dollars between us. We were flush. That last "get the fuck off my porch" was our signal that departure time was upon us. Who needs this belligerent, icy shit, right?

Jerry owned a seriously beat up 1950 Oldsmobile that burned a quart of oil every 100 miles and had a broken hood latch that tended periodically to slam the hood up against the windshield like a huge metallic bat once the car was going more than 40 miles an hour. And for those few seconds, blinded by the bat hood until we could pull to the side of the highway to tie it down again, we had no idea what over-the-road Peterbilt behemoth might be rushing toward us bringing instant and permanent disfigurement. Or death, with our teeth, hair and eyeballs scattered all over the highway. Solution? Tie the goddam hood down with a length of deck rope, which meant in winter we had to pry the ice off and untie the frozen knot every time we needed to add a quart of oil, which was every 100 miles. It was the perfect vehicle to get us to Clearwater, Florida, more than a thousand miles away.

We agreed to meet later that night at my place after packing our suitcases (I had one now). We decided to leave a note that told whoever found it that we were in the wind for places unknown and adventures unbound. The high school? The classes? The fact of truancy? To hell with all that. Life is short, right? Live free or die! I had snatched a handful of my mother's diet pills – amphetamines - or as we called the cute little colorful capsules, Christmas Trees, two weeks earlier during my last visit. Jerry was impatiently honking his horn as I locked the door to my room, put the key in my wallet, and without a last look at my "home" quietly walked down the stairway. It was 10 o'clock at night. The snowstorm that had developed that afternoon was now growing into an Ohio-style blizzard. We looked at our Texaco road map and figured we would be out of the winter weather and into the roads that snaked through the mountains of Kentucky just about daybreak. He slid over to the passenger's side as I walked around the front of the car, checking the already frozen knot that was holding down the fly-away hood. I could smell the rancid odor of Old Grandad as we drove off.

"Jesus, man, do you have to drink that rot-gut crap?" Truth was, his drinking irritated the hell out of me. Jerry was only seventeen, but already had developed that alcoholic's belligerence and would be the first to throw a punch in a barroom argument no matter the odds against him.

"Hey, don't fucking talk like my mom," he said.

"You drink around your mother?"

"Sure. But she's usually loaded herself. Drive on, my man. Wake me up when I can smell salt water."

I felt like we were going to pass through a dangerous foreign country. The "South" was that huge jumble of roads and small towns between Ohio and Florida. Florida wasn't part of the South. Florida was where older people from cities like Cleveland or Detroit or New York moved to escape the brutal northern winters. The actual South, the scary South, was what filled the distance between here and there, filled it with the KKK and Rebel flags and religious nut-cases and segregation and dirt farmers and dark country roads where all sorts of evil shit transpired and people who talked weird and said stuff that made no sense at all except when they were bragging about their guns or how much fun it was to terrorize Negroes.

And the Southern girls? The white ones? Oh, sweet Jesus. We knew they were all beautiful and all they wanted, every one of them, more than anything else ever, was a chance to have sex with a Yankee boy. I don't know how or why we knew that.

27

We just did.

The weather was getting worse. Blinding snow and pin-point sleet slicing parallel to the ground, reflected in the glare of the oncoming headlights, reduced visibility to 25 yards at best. The wind outside shrieked like a dying banshee. The roads were glass. I was driving. No way in hell I would trust my life with Jerry behind the wheel, drunk or sober, in weather like this. And, anyway, his license had been suspended for some shit last Fall. I had no idea what. I had yet to get a driver's license and I knew that if the state police stopped us we were fucked. Juvenile delinquents for sure, who probably robbed a gas station back up the road where we left several dead bodies.

Every few minutes the Olds would lurch to the left as another icy blast, blowing over the dark, dead cornfields tried to push us across the narrow highway's yellow line into a head-on collision. We were on US 25, a two-lane road that had an Interstate highway in its future. A few stretches were already built and open. But US 25 – the Dixie Highway - was the route we would travel for most of the night. We drove past Findlay, Ohio, the home to both my parents, and the feeling that I was driving through my family's tangled history blew over me like the snow and the wind screaming outside the car. Jerry was starting to nod out from the booze he had been steadily drinking since we left Toledo two hours ago. We had come all of 45 miles. I wanted him to stay up front and talk, keep me awake. The driving snow and the jerky dance of oncoming headlights was becoming hypnotic.

"C'mon, man," I said. "Don't fucking pass out. Tell me about your great-aunt. What's her story?"

"What's her *story*?"

"Yeah, you know, why's she in Clearwater? How old is she?

Is the house near the beach? Shit like that . . ."

No use. He pulled himself over the front seat into the back pushing the suitcases onto the floor. "Hey, she's old. Real old. A couple of blocks from the beach. She's got a boyfriend, some old man in his 90s. Who gives a shit?"

He fell asleep, his six-foot-two frame bent nearly double in the back seat. Okay, fuck it. If I fall asleep at the wheel it's his fault. It was time to swallow one of Sylvia's dexies. *Zoom-zoom.* The radio worked and didn't smell like rancid whiskey breath, so go ahead, Jerry. Climb your ass in back and leave me alone to slide my way to the ocean. I'll listen to the goddam radio. I tuned to CKLW, a Canadian pop station in Windsor, Ontario, across the river from Detroit. A doo-wop song was playing, with the tight *a capella* harmonies that were so familiar to anyone growing up in the 50s. The music made me homesick. Two hours south and I'm homesick. When the attic was still home, I'd get together on the corner after supper with boys from the neighborhood to sing our own doo-wop. We'd figure out the harmonies from the songs we heard on the radio. The black kids would assign each of us our parts and demonstrate how it was to be sung because they said the white boys didn't know shit about singing, much less how to arrange harmonies that didn't sound like people singing different songs at the same time. I guessed that was probably because most white people didn't learn to sing in church the way black kids did, the way church singing was supposed to sound. Especially not in a Catholic church where everything was dark and funereal and filled with statues of saints who had all been tortured or beheaded or crucified and where any cheerful harmonies would not be tolerated. Was there no joy in this religion unless a statue's marble hands started bleeding?

29

That would be a sure sign from Jesus that he was checking in, making sure the faithful could still be occasionally goosed into sobbing insistence that the Messiah was coming, the Messiah was coming! A real jokester, that Jesus. So, nobody sang in the Catholic church except the choir and the choir was as dreary as the church. Singing made too much noise and the words were in English, not Latin, so where was the mystery? The black kids said white church singing sounded like a choir made of zombies.

Singing in a black church – *halleluiah!* - was way different; foot-stomping, hand-clapping, arm-waving, testifying, swelling organ music, the preacher pimp-stepping across the front of the sanctuary, shouts to Heaven, the men in the amen corner on their feet dancing. They were making that "joyful noise unto the Lord," while, in the white Catholic churches the moaning zombies were ruining *"Eat This Bread,"* or *"Dust and Ashes,"* or a real favorite of the Polish immigrants, *"Juz Ad Rona,"* dedicated to "Our Lady of Sorrows, Queen of Poland." Of course she was.

CKLW's signal caught up with us just as the Skyliners were getting into *"Since I Don't Have You,"* a slow-dance favorite because, if you were cool about it, you could brush against your girl's pointy tits without being accused of copping a feel. Of course, it was the bra that was pointy, not her breasts, but no matter: a feel is a feel. The night wore on. The snowstorm eased and gradually I could see the lights of a roadside gas station and the purplish halo of neon surrounding the attached Greyhound bus station. I had to pee and I guessed Jerry did too after all the booze.

"Hey! Wake up! I gotta take a leak. Wake your ass up!"

"We in Florida?"

"Yeah, this is Tampa. Can't you see the palm trees? The snow's just an illusion. Fuck no, we're not in Florida! And the temperature gauge says we're about to blow the engine."

He sat up. "How many miles have we gone?"

"The last sign I could read said Dayton's about 10 miles, so about 90 miles."

"And you didn't put in some oil yet? No shit, we're going to blow the engine . . . *you're* going to blow the engine! Every 50 miles, remember? Oil!'"

The thing about Jerry was he could irritate the hell out me very easily, even though he was my best friend. I pulled off the highway into the tiny, lighted parking lot of the bus station/roadside diner combination, parked and went inside. A line of passengers was moving slowly out the door and back onto one of the two idling buses. I wondered where they all were going; an old black man, parents with sleeping children in their arms, a couple of sailors, a young white woman carrying a sandwich and a movie fan magazine, all being checked by the driver to make sure the people getting on were the same ones who got off a half hour ago. The sign on the front of the bus said Chicago. I wanted to warn the driver about the storm we had just come through, but I guessed he already knew.

I went inside while Jerry dug around in the trunk where we'd put a case of cheap oil, a screwdriver, and a hammer before we left Toledo. When I came out, he was banging away at the ball of filthy ice that covered the thick knot holding the hood closed. We finally got it open and poured four quarts of oil into the steaming engine. It was Jerry's turn to take a leak.

One at a time, the two buses pulled away from the station leaving behind a cloud of diesel fumes that had a sad middle-of-the-night smell. I remembered that smell from riding the

Greyhound from Toledo to Findlay on one of the frequent trips Silvia and I and my brothers and sister made to get away from Joe's madness. It was a memory that made tears start to well up and I quickly brushed them away. No fucking way I'd let Jerry see me cry. He came out to the parking lot carrying a pack of rubbers.

"Three for a quarter, right?" He held them up and I saw the "sold for the prevention of disease only" bullshit on the label.

"Really?" I said. "You plan on getting laid? With a Southern girl? And then have some of those good ol' Southern boys stomp you to death and feed your broken body to the alligators? C'mon, man, get in the car and let's go. We're almost there. Only a thousand miles to go in this shit-bucket you call a car."

"Hey, don't worry about it," he grinned. "I was a Boy Scout, right? 'Be prepared,' right?" He waved the pocket-size packet in my face.

"You think the Boy Scouts meant be prepared to get laid? Is there a merit badge for pussy?"

"Funny. A man's gotta take responsibility . . ."

"Don't say 'right' again. You end every sentence with 'right?' Your making me crazy."

"Okay. How about 'fuck you?' Can I say that again?"

"Jerry, go back to sleep, pal. You're getting a wee bit irritating and we still have a long way to go . . . right?"

The hypnotic miles droned on. We passed through the few remaining small Ohio towns north of Cincinnati, and finally the big city itself. Directly ahead, across the Ohio River was the beginning of The South. It was five o'clock in the morning when I drove through Covington, Kentucky. The rumors in Toledo said if you wanted to get laid easily and with no hassle from the cops, Covington was the place. It was wall-to-wall prostitutes, the biggest open-to-the-skies whorehouse east of the Mississippi. I kept looking, driving slowly through the dark, snow-packed city. There was not a hooker to be seen, probably because of the snow.

On the edge of downtown Covington, I saw the first clue that Jerry and I were in a place entirely different from Toledo. A neon sign in front of the Dixie Highway Motor Hotel was simple and direct: WHITE ONLY NO COLORED. Holy shit! There it was. "No colored." The segregation I knew about, but had never seen in such a public display, was right there. On that sign. Anybody could see it. And, it meant my black friends back in high school couldn't spend a night in this shitty run-down motor hotel just 200 miles south of Toledo, because they were colored. So, where did black people stay when they were travelling? Were the motels reserved for colored people somewhere down a side street, hidden so as not to offend white people?

Fuck the motels. Another stupid example of the half-assed attitudes that decided who was on the top and who was on the bottom; who had power and who didn't. Black travelers would just have to sleep wherever they could. I had heard of and read about the real terror that blacks dealt with in the South, the real violence. A couple of years earlier it was the murder of a young black kid, Emmett Till, that shocked the hell out of us. He was from Chicago and had been visiting family in Mississippi. At a local grocery store where he had stopped to buy a bottle of soda he spoke to the white woman who owned the store. She claimed he had gotten "fresh." A few nights later her husband and another white man went to the relative's house – where Emmett was staying – and took the 14-year-old away. They beat and mutilated him almost beyond recognition and then shot him and threw his body into the Tallahatchie River. Three days later his bloated corpse was discovered, tangled in weeds and broken tree limbs.

Till's body was returned to Chicago. His mother insisted on a public funeral service with an open casket to show the world the brutality of the killing. The funeral, with photos of Till's battered remains on the front pages of newspapers around the world, exposed the lie her son's murder laid bare. There for the world to see was not only the horror and barbarism of racism in the U.S., but also the hypocrisy found on the walls of nearly every elementary school in America: *"We hold these truths to be self-evident; that all men are created equal, that they are endowed by their Creator with certain unalienable rights, that among these are life, liberty, and the pursuit of happiness."*

What painful, ugly words that every black person in the U.S. knew was a lie. And the whites eventually saw the lie, too, even if we didn't admit it. We couldn't admit it. And, if we did, so what? Who was going to change things? I woke Jerry, who looked as though he had been dead for about a week.

"Wake up! Get your ass outta bed! You'll be late for school." A muffled "fuck you" was my answer. Always with the "fuck you."

"C'mon, man. Wake up. Let's get some coffee." He sat up and squinted in the glare of the night's foot of new snow. "Where are we?"

"In the South, Jer. The honest-to-god South. You should have seen the sign a few blocks back. 'Whites only' at one of those cheesy road hotels."

"No shit? Where are we, Alabama?"

"Kentucky."

"What time is it?" He reached for a cigarette.

"About five A-M."

"And we're only in Kentucky? How slow are you driving?"

"Slow enough to keep us alive, fast enough to outrun your bullshit."

The Dexedrine had been percolating for a couple of hours. The buzz had peaked and was starting to level off. Oh, no. We'll have none of that shit. I wanted some coffee so I could swallow another one.

"Look, man, you wanna drive?"

I was counting on a "no." Jerry liked to drive on the wrong side of the road until he heard the frantic honking of a car coming from the opposite direction. It was a game he played just to see the look of terror on the other driver's face as they sped past each other.

"No, my license's suspended, remember? You're doin' fine, my man. Just get us there."

I pulled into a White Tower parking lot. The place was already open and serving breakfast. We went inside after we hacked the ice off the knot holding the hood down and poured another three quarts of oil into the engine. At the restaurant's entrance, a small metal sign was attached to the building. You couldn't miss it. "Colored Served. Carry Out Only." Progress, right?

We were back on the road in ten minutes. I swallowed another Dexie and chased it with coffee that had the faint taste of overcooked hamburgers even though I knew the coffee could never catch my little Christmas trees. *Zoom, zoom.*

As we got further into Kentucky, the highway's gentle rises and dips became steeper and more sudden, the curves sharper. The snow had stopped several miles back and the Dixie Highway was now two-lane twists and hairpin turns. At least it was dry and, after miles of blinding snow, dark. Very dark. No roadside anything. Just dark shadows of the massive oaks and pine trees that leaned over the road like arms trying to snatch us into the darkness. I drove on towards Lexington. By the time we got there we would have a bit of misty, filtered daylight.

A few miles of the road's sharp downhill turns and my hands were getting sweaty from the death grip I had on the steering wheel. The tires would vibrate and then squeal when I took the curves too fast. Every few moments Jerry would moan, "You're going to kill us. Slow down. Oh, god . . . not Kentucky. Don't let me die in Kentucky. Somebody help me . . . *you're gonna drive us over a cliff . . . help . . .*" Oh, for Christ's sake. I dropped my voice several levels and moaned back at him, "Jerry! I am Satan! I am here to take you home. *You are going to die!*"

By now the Dexedrine and coffee combo was working its magic. Everything was again beautiful, even though I couldn't see shit. The black sky was beautiful! The shadows were beautiful! The white line in the middle of the road was beautiful! I wanted to sing! I made a mental note to send Silvia a thank you letter for having diet pills in her medicine cabinet. Next stop, I'll write her a nice note of thanks, put it in a beautiful card and drop it at the nearest post office.

The road was an endless dark tunnel, the music was pumping, and the Dexies were driving little bolts of warm lightning up and down my arms. Perfect. Down the highway we went, the Olds a warm cocoon that was snug and safe and beginning to smell like a flophouse.

Driving through Kentucky's alien darkness, I thought about a crazed incident from a couple of months earlier, November to be exact. It caused an intense moment at our high school and I couldn't help but sort through it all once again. I knew I'd never forget it.

It was the end of football season. I was on the team, second-string fullback. Second string because my best time in those killer 50-yard wind sprints the coach insisted on was 12 seconds. The starting fullback was a big kid named Troy Johnson who could do it in 9 seconds and change. Every game, I sat on the bench feeling guilty as hell because I kept hoping Troy wouldn't get up after a tackle and coach would call my name. "Mike! Get in there and move the ball!" It seemed Troy was made of black concrete. The players who tackled him were the ones who had a tough time getting up.

I got into four games that year, but only after we were at least three touchdowns ahead and there was less than two minutes of playing time left on the clock. Ours was a kick-ass team and we wound up second in the city's high school league. It was a tough league. For the most part, the players were all sons of foundry workers and drop-forge operators and tool and die makers, each of whom took pride in watching their sons kicking the other team's asses. At Scott High all the players got to wear their team jerseys on Fridays, pep rally day. Mine had the big number 42 on the back, which immediately identified me as a warrior who would bring glory to the school and girls to my one-room apartment.

During the pre-game rallies, I sat in the semi-circle of metal chairs arranged on the field house floor along with my team mates while the student body assembled in the stands went ape shit and screamed for victory that night, if not the other team's total dismemberment. I loved it. Being on the team and wearing that jersey every Friday made me almost normal to the students who couldn't understand my living alone. I was different from them. Radically so. They knew it; I knew it. No family, no household chores, no vacation trips, just me alone. And that scared the other kids' parents. What did I do living alone like that? Who told me when to go to bed, to get up, do my homework? Who made sure I didn't go all juvenile delinquent? Who fixed my meals? Who did my laundry? And the parents with daughters were particularly concerned. How could the school board allow such a thing? The girls' prime directive was: "Don't you dare go near his apartment or your grounded for life!" Which, of course, made the girls even more curious and determined to check me out. And they did. Thank you, terrified parents.

It was tradition at Scott High to elect our Homecoming Queen before the last game of the year, the Thanksgiving Day contest against our cross-town rival, Waite High School. For years, the voting was by football players only, but this particular year it was decided the entire Senior Class would get to choose the Queen. The election was held the week before the big game and the winner was announced over the PA system right before school was dismissed for the day. Her name was Sharon Parker and she was the perfect choice. An honor student, active in all sorts of school activities, and, by white standards, beautiful. She also was the first black girl at Scott High School to be elected Queen.

We were a fully integrated student body as were all the public schools in Toledo. Our school friendships crossed racial differences easily and often. All the sports teams and academic clubs were a mix of black and white. It was considered stupid and trashy to show even a hint of racism, and god have mercy on any white kid who said "nigger," or any black kid who said, "honky" or "cracker." You were immediately labeled a total asshole and no one would hang out with you. You ate your lunch alone for weeks until your punishment was considered adequate. And, even then, it was a bit risky to be seen talking with you. Tough rules. But the administration told us on the first day of each school year that we were there for more than just academics; we were to learn "tolerance." The idea of "respect" would follow. That was the hope. The school faculty knew the country was changing and the changes were going to be difficult to adjust to. The potential for disruption came from the Supreme Court ruling a couple years earlier, the decision that said racial segregation in the schools was unconstitutional. The rules we were trying to live by were new and were causing absolute resistance across the country, the Northern as well as the Southern states. No one was certain how to proceed, but the requirement to obey the law was absolute and the federal government had made it clear it would, and did, use the military to enforce the Court's ruling.

The announcement of Sharon's selection as Homecoming Queen was made on a Friday afternoon just before the final bell. The weekend would provide enough time to let the reality sink in. "A black Homecoming Queen! Holy shit!" the white kids said. "A black Homecoming Queen! Holy shit!" the black kids said. It was a remarkable day, no matter your race.

Monday arrived.

The usual morning ritual included the seniors gathering under the massive oak tree that shaded the full-size stone and metal replica of the Liberty Bell directly in front of the school's main entrance. The air was thick with cigarette smoke and chatter as we bullshitted each other about all the cool things we did over the weekend, most of it lies. But, not this Monday.

39

When I got to the bell the conversation was muted. Students were craning their necks to look up into the tree's branches. What the hell?

"What's going on?" I asked the first kid I met. It was Troy, the first-string fullback, the one made of black concrete.

"Are you kidding?"

"No, gimme a clue, okay?"

"Look up in the fucking tree, Malloy."

Oh, shit. There it was. Forty feet up, swinging back and forth in the morning breeze. A slapped together effigy. A laundry bag full of rags with scraggly terry cloth arms and legs attached. A rope was around the thing's neck. The face was painted black. It was wearing what looked like a white dress from the Salvation Army. There was a sign hanging loosely from its mid-section. The sign said, *"Homecoming Queen."* A self-segregation was happening under the tree. The black kids were huddled together in small groups, talking softly and shaking their heads. The white kids seemed to be in a state of total embarrassment. Their quiet exclamations of shame rippled through the knots of obviously shocked 17-year-olds, too young to understand the full scope of what the effigy represented, too unprepared for the ugliness that had now made its presence known in what the kids had considered, with more than a little smugness, a small enclave free from racial bullshit. "We're not Mississippi," was a standard answer when asked how everybody seemed to respect each other at Scott High. "We're not like those bigots in Alabama and Georgia! We respect each other. We are not racists!" The declarations now seemed ridiculous given what was swinging back and forth over our heads.

Before classes began that sad and shocking day, the responsibility of trying to reassure the students that, no, we were not bigoted thugs, belonged to the Principal, a professorial type who seemed always to be zig-zagging through halls, barely avoiding colliding with students changing classes, seemingly on his way to a very important meeting just like Alice's White Rabbit. He had a prominent nose so, of course, we called him The Beak. His message was heart-felt, and we could hear his voice slightly break a couple of times as it came over each room's PA speaker. He said whoever had so deeply violated the spirit of community at Scott High School would not be punished but instead would be asked to publicly apologize and to explain why they had lofted a raggedy-ass caricature of our Homecoming Queen into the upper limbs of the tree, and, most important, what they thought the outcome would be. We didn't yet have the word "racist" in our vocabulary. If you were white and didn't want to hang out with the black kids you were considered "prejudiced," not racist. We knew that prejudice could result in people being killed, their homes burned, their churches bombed. But we also knew that particular madness happened far away from Toledo, Ohio. So, why was this gruesome effigy of our Homecoming Queen hanging from a branch in the tallest oak tree on campus?

No one saw it happen, but when classes were dismissed, and everyone rushed to the front of the school to look at "it" again, the effigy had been removed. Later that week the boys who had hung it – and, thank god, they weren't on the football team - made their apologies, suffered their short-lived humiliation, but later, away from The Beak, laughed and made jokes about how their names and what they had done that day would live forever in the school's history.

Chapter 5

Lexington

The highway mileage signs were ticking off the distance to Lexington. A hundred, eighty-six, seventy. The car twisted and turned through the looming mountains and inky hollows. An occasional semi would roar by, usually when the sheer mountain drop-offs were on my side of the road. The semi's wake would cause the car to shudder and drift toward the ridiculous little pretend fence that skirted the edge of the road, the only barricade between us and the void that ended 300 feet down. Straight down. Jerry slept through it all, deep in the arms of Morpheus, snoring and farting, and the occasional piteous moan.

The only available light, other than passing headlights, came from bare bulbs attached to the weathered fronts of closed auto repair shacks. They cast muddy light on hand-painted, often misspelled signs nailed to the buildings: "Breedlove's Car Repare," "Stop And Go Engine Fixing," "Junk Car Parts." And, almost visible as we passed, the more professional look of the threatening religious messages, always framed as a question: "Jesus Saves, Are You Ready?" or "Where Will You

Spend Eternity, Heaven or The Fires Of Hell?" or "Are You Saved? Are You Sure?" or "Are You Ready for The Rapture?" or "Do You Know Jesus? He Knows You and He Sees Everything!" The messages strained against the roadside gloom like chained goblins. I had decided religion, all religion, was bullshit after finding out what the crazed God of Abraham had visited upon his chosen people with the Holocaust. I didn't know the details, but I felt as though the details were unnecessary. A god who would order the deaths of millions of men, women, children, babies, old people, for no apparent reason was a god who, in the process of condemning so many innocent millions, had committed suicide. Anyone who insisted such a degenerate beast was in fact a benevolent creator was as insane as the beast itself. With a couple of exceptions: my maternal grandparents.

When I was a kid, I spent most of my summers with Angelo and Laura. They had converted from Catholicism to Protestantism because being Italian immigrants in a small Ohio town was risky enough. There was always the suspicion they might be Anarchists, ready to set off their hidden bombs when the signal came from headquarters somewhere in Sicily. Why add the threat of being Papists, worshippers of graven images, whose priests made weird hand motions and chanted in an occult language not at all like the English Jesus surely spoke. Foreigners only caused trouble. Especially non-white foreigners, Italians being the perfect example. Silvia told me how embarrassed she felt when, one day in the fourth grade during recess, a classmate insisted, "Your dad carries a knife in his belt, doesn't he!"

"No," she answered. "Why do you think my dad carries a knife?"

"Cuz my pop says all Dagoes carry knives!"

"My dad's not a Dago."

"Yes, he is!"

"No, he isn't and that's a bad word. I'm gonna tell the teacher you said it and you'll probably be expelled!"

"And you're one, too."

"No, I'm not!"

"Are too! Dago!"

At which point Silvia would start crying, feeling the sting of being insulted for her skin color, for being a Dago, for being foreign. In her eighth-grade class photograph she is at once noticeable. She's standing a few inches away from the other students, her dark skin made darker by the white graduation dress. There she was, the single "colored" girl in the school.

Silvia's parents were church-goers. Twice on Sundays and prayer meeting every Wednesday night. During my summer visits the mid-week trips to Calvary Baptist Church gave me a chance to watch people praying with a fervency that I couldn't help but marvel at. Did they really believe some Sky Spook was listening to them, with their shouting and trembling? Did they really expect the Hairy Thunderer to drop whatever He was doing, wherever He was doing it, maybe in Africa where He was really busy healing all those millions of lepers and then making sure everybody had enough to eat, drop it all and rush halfway around the world to Findlay, Ohio, find the Calvary Baptist Church, and seriously listen to this hysteria? Yeah, they did.

The prayer meetings took place in one of the church's dusty, hot, upper rooms. I was the only kid there and while the group of adults each took his or her turn, on their knees, their backs to the middle of the prayer circle, hands folded on the wooden seats of the ladder-back chairs, I watched the dust motes floating in the early evening sunlight that filtered into the room through the stained, grimy windows. Not stained-glass windows. That was for wealthy congregations, like Catholics. Calvary Baptist windows were just stained.

They prayed for everything: Their sick relatives, the recently dead, the soon-to-be dead, the souls lost to alcohol, the non-believers, President Truman, themselves. On and on it went, each one in turn. When it came my grandparents' turn, there was no loud wailing, no pleading exhortations, no tears. Angelo and Laura made quiet prayers. God forbid, so to speak, they would make a spectacle of themselves, even in this moldy upper room within a circle of their God-fearing friends. And, they were quick. No extraneous bullshit like praying for President Truman. Just quickly hit the high spots: relatives, health issues, the drunks, the unsaved and on to the Amen.

I never told Laura I was an atheist, that I knew there was no such thing as god, or heaven, or angels, or answered prayers. I knew these things because if there was a god how could he be so fucking cruel? Wars, famines, diseases, hatred, death, all of it could have been stopped with the wave of his heavenly hand, a nod of his precious head. And, on a lower level, why would god allow Joe to beat us kids and Silvia simply because he was insane? I loved my grandma, for sure, but, *god?* No. It was all bullshit and I wanted to tell her that even though I knew she wouldn't have listened and probably would have taken one of her mulberry-bush switches and whipped the devil out of me. The literal Devil. She would have understood and appreciated the Kentucky roadside signs that warned of the horrors awaiting the unsaved. I hope she was welcomed when she arrived at the gates to her heaven.

Finally, Lexington. Daylight had started prying open cracks

in the sullen skies an hour ago. The snow was piled high at the sides of the street and it was obvious the city had gotten a heavy blast of winter. I had been driving for what seemed like forever and needed a break. Jerry was waking up in the back seat and the noises he was making were a symphony of nasty sounds: farts, belches, yawns, a throat clearing that sounded like he was trying to bring up marbles. I was looking for a place to get breakfast. "Hey, let's get something to eat. Maybe a HoJo's?"

"Works for me," he answered. "So, where are we?"

"Lexington, Kentucky, my man. You slept through a fun drive coming over those mountains."

"Yeah? That must have been when I dreamed I was falling into a bottomless hole. I gotta piss."

So did I. We pulled into a Howard Johnson's parking lot and went inside. While Jerry made a dash for the john, I ordered coffee and tried to stop my hands from shaking. That's the thing about Dexedrine; super intense highs, but very twitchy landings.

The waitress gave me a bright red smile as she placed two cups and a pot of coffee on the table of the corner booth I had sunk into. We were her only customers. The place was empty, and the smell of frying bacon made me hungry despite the Christmas Trees.

"You and your friend look like you've come a ways. . ." She was being polite. Both Jerry and I looked like warmed-over death. She could have added, ". . . from a cemetery."

She had dark hair and deep blue eyes. Short, pixie hair-style, slim body, no question a former high school cheerleader or majorette, a visual blessing after hours of driving through relentless snow and unfamiliar darkness. She looked vaguely familiar. I wanted her to keep talking in that soft Southern voice.

"Yes, ma'm. We're travelers. On our way to Clearwater, Florida." I was trying to be pleasant enough to keep her attention. "Been driving all night. It was rough, believe me"

"Well, we'll fix y'all right up. Be back with a menu soon as your friend comes out. Shouldn't you boys be in school?"

"We're college students. It's the semester break. We're gonna get some sun," I lied.

"College students, off to have fun. Well, I'll be right back." Y'all. She said *"y'all."*

Jerry came out and slid into the booth. "You order yet? Did you see that waitress?"

"Nope. Waiting for you. I've got manners. Of course I saw her. How do you think the coffee got here?"

He had pushed water through his hair to smooth it down and the result, along with the dark circles under his eyes, made him look like a dead raccoon. When the waitress returned – her name tag said "Connie" – we ordered the breakfast special. Eggs, grits, bacon, sausage, toast, and southern-style potatoes. Neither of us knew what grits were, but they were on the menu with just about every meal combination, breakfast, lunch, and dinner. Connie laughed and said they were made from mashed up corn. She pronounced it *"mayshed."*

"You boys are Yankees, I reckon?"

Jerry answered immediately. "Yup. We're from a long way from here, Toledo, Ohio. We're Yankees all right. Toledo could be part of Michigan, we're so close. You ever been to Toledo? We make all the glass that's in this restaurant, probably. That's what we're famous for." I watched his bloodshot eyes as he watched the loose buttons at the top of her tight HoJo tunic.

47

That was Jerry's M.O.: Talk fast, keep it loose, distract your prey, move in, bingo! Success! You're gonna get laid!

She half-smiled at Jerry's verbal torrent. "Y'all talk fast, too. So, you're on your way to Florida. I was there once before I got divorced. I love the ocean."

"Yeah, me too," Jerry said before she finished saying "ocean." Which was complete bullshit. Neither of us had ever been near an ocean, much less been in one. He kept going.

"I love walking in the sand, you know, barefoot. How 'bout you? It's tickle-y, right?"

"Tickle-y? Well, it's not tickle-y when you get it into the bottom of your bathing suit. More like gritty." Yeah, she was playing, too, strumming Jerry like a banjo. "You ever get sand in your bathing suit?"

He stopped scraping grape jelly out of the little packet and onto his toast and looked up at her.

"Oh, yeah, I have. I really have. And you know what?"
Whut . . .?"

"That's when I take my trunks off and go in the water naked!" Jerry was deep in the game. An expert working his way to a few minutes of early morning sex in the back room.

Connie grinned. "Well, Ah'll be. Nekkid, huh? Yeah, I've done that. I love to swim nekkid, usually in the river, but Ah'll bet it feels good in the ocean and all. But I'd be a little afraid somethin' might come up and bite me. I'd hate for somethin' to bite me, 'specially if Ah'm nekkid. But, I cain't wait for summer. Anything ever bit you?"

Jerry had stopped eating. For a second, I thought he'd stopped breathing. Like I had.

"In the ocean?" he asked. I decided to stay silent, afraid my throat would slam shut if I even *tried* to talk.

"Or . . . anywhere," she said with a wicked smile. "You know . . . a bite's a bite, right? Little ol' teeth marks . . "

Before he could answer, the bell over the entrance rang signaling someone had come in. Goddammit!

"Gotta tend to business, boys. Be back in a minute." She turned and walked toward the front of the restaurant. A black man had entered and stood waiting at the end of the long, white counter. Connie was half-way there when she stopped and put her hands on her hips.

"What do you want in here?" she said, louder than necessary.

"Yes'um. I wanted to get a cup of coffee cuz it's awful cold out there, and . . ." Connie interrupted him, "You know you're not allowed in here. You know that!"

"Yes'um, I do, I really do. But, just a cup of coffee or even hot water will do. In one of those cardboard cups so I don't get nothin' dirty."

Jerry and I stared at this pitiful little drama and the Connie that had emerged.

"James Lewis, you've been told not to enter this restaurant. Do you want me to call the police? If you want a cup of hot water, go around in back and wait. I've got customers in here."

"Yes'um. I surely will. Around in back. Yes'um."

He turned and walked out. We watched through the plate glass window as he moved slowly along the side of the building and disappeared. Connie came back to our booth.

"Sorry about that, boys. We've old him over and over not to come in and he just won't listen."

"Why can't he come in," I asked? "He just wanted coffee."

Connie wiped her hands on the front of her apron and looked at me as if I were the stupidest son-of-a-bitch on earth.

"Why? Well, if we let that one come in, then every nigger in Lexington will say, 'Let's go over to that Howard Johnson's. They serve colored people.' And then what? We lose our business, that's what. White folks won't eat where niggers have used the silverware. So, no, he can't come in here. None of 'em can." The conversation about swimming naked had evaporated. She went on. "See, what it is, you boys aren't from here so you don't know what our laws are. We have to have it this way. They've got nigger restaurants on the south side of town. He could go there if he's so cold."

A black man in Lexington, Kentucky, couldn't get a cup of coffee in a Howard Johnson's on a freezing morning? In a paper cup? Not even a real cup, a fucking paper cup?

"Boys, I gotta get to work." She laid the check on the table and scooped up our plates and silverware. "Nice talking with y'all. Have a good trip. Wish I was goin' with you." Jerry's head jerked up.

"But . . . gotta stay here and work. Got a kid at home, and no husband. Sorta' makes things a little more difficult, you know what I mean? And you . . . (she pointed at Jerry), don't let too much sand get in your swimmin' britches!" We stood and put our coats on.

I laid three dollars and five cents on the table and walked out. The three dollars was for breakfast. The nickel was for Connie.

Chapter 6

Colored Ice Cream

I drove slowly down Main Street. Slowly, because I damn sure didn't want to get pulled over by a Lexington cop. "No license, boys? You are driving through my city with no license?" And then off to jail where we'd be beaten, sodomized, and disappeared. Our families would never find us. That's what happened in Southern jails, especially to Yankee boys who were obviously up to no good whatsoever. We knew this because we had seen the movie, *I Am A Fugitive From A Chain Gang.* Nothing but gruesome shit would happen to us if we vanished into a Southern jail.

Jerry was sitting up front, very uncomfortable with the hard-on he still had from playing verbal grab-ass with Connie.

"Would you fuck her, Malloy? I would have. Damn, she was sexy, right? And divorced! You know what that means, right?"

"No. What does it mean?"

"It means she's experienced. And once they're experienced they gotta have sex or they'll go crazy! Gotta have it! That's the way women are."

"And you think she wanted to do you?"

"Hey, I could tell. She was looking at me with that gotta have it look."

"You're out of your crawl space, pal. She no more wanted to fuck you than that old man who came in."

"That's bullshit. She wanted me. I could see it all over her face. I'm serious, a divorced woman's got to get the dick. It's, like, a rule."

"Isn't your mom divorced?"

"That's different, asshole. But, as long as we're on the subject, have you gotten laid yet, or are you still just jerking off? I bet you're still a virgin, right? I know what I'm talking about, trust me, about divorced women. They gotta screw or they'll flip out, maybe commit suicide. For real."

Jerry's "for reals" were always borderline ridiculous. I never could figure out where he got his information. But, it was part of his charm.

"Thanks for the education, dude. I wouldn't know shit if you didn't enlighten me. You ought to teach a class. Call it *'The Sex Like Of The Divorced Woman, Except My Mother.'* And, whether or not I'm getting laid is my business. You think I haven't had chicks in my apartment? Gimme a fucking break."

"Have you? The guys think you're getting pussy every night. You're getting quite a rep, my man. So? Are you?"

"Right, Jer, every night. I fuck 'em all, the long, the short, and the tall."

"I know you're lying, right?"

Yeah, I was still a virgin, but I'd never admit it to Jerry. All that opportunity to get laid that comes with living alone and I hadn't yet figured out how to convince a girl to come to my room to, you know, help me with my Latin homework. There was a Catholic girls' school – Notre Dame Academy – across the street from my rooming house so it should have been easy, especially Wednesday nights after the little darlings had gone to Confession. The priest would tell them to say the requisite *Hail Marys* or *Our Fathers* and once through that bullshit ritual they would be cleared to do all sorts of nasty stuff for another week. In that regard, Catholicism was great! A free pass every Wednesday.

A block from Notre Dame Academy there was a drug store with the requisite soda fountain and a jukebox that had all the latest rock and roll songs. The girls would hang out there after Confession enjoying a few minutes of teen-age normalcy and a vanilla Coke until their curfew approached. Then the nuns would come out, stand in front of the school's iron gates, and blow their shrill whistles. Like Pavlov's dogs the girls would march out of the soda shop, back up the street, through the gates and into the courtyard of the gray, medieval-looking cluster of stone buildings, while I stood on the opposite corner with what I hoped was a look of both lust and experience, waiting for a couple of them to run across the street, grab my arms, and demand we go up to my room and have wild sex. If only I had the magic words, especially if they were in Latin.

We were running out of Main Street and about to rejoin the Dixie Highway when we saw him standing on the curb, half hidden in the deep morning shadows. His shoulders were drawn up against the cold, hands stuffed into his jacket pockets, a muffler drawn tight around his neck. A small duffel bag and a guitar case leaned against a street sign sticking up out of the snow. As we got closer he un-hunched his shoulders and thrust out his thumb.

"Wanna pick him up? He looks like he's freezing his ass off."

"I dunno. What do you think?" Jerry answered. "What if

53

he's an escaped convict, you know, a murderer. Then what do we do?"

"A murderer? A prison escapee? With a guitar and a duffel bag? Gimme a fucking break, pal. Do you want to pick him up or not? I don't think a colored guy hitchin' in the South has much of a chance getting a ride. And, we might be saving his life, right?"

"Up to you, man. You're driving."

"Yeah, but if he's a killer he'll get both of us."

"We can put him in the back seat. If he tries to kill one of us, the other one can grab him and knock the shit out of him."

"Sounds like a plan, Jer."

I pulled to the side of the street, up against a bank of snow that had been pushed to the side by a snow plow. Jerry opened the passenger side rear door.

"C'mon in! You're turning blue!" Jerry cracked up. That was some funny shit. A colored guy turning blue.

He climbed over the top of the snow bank and slid down to the open door, duffel and guitar case dragging snow with him.

"Wow, man. Thank you for stopping! Thought I was gonna freeze to death." He was checking out his potential ride, looking quickly from the front seat to the back. I know what he was thinking. What if we were murderers, escaped convicts who had stolen this shit-box of a car and were looking for more victims? He decided to risk it all. He pushed his duffel and guitar case into the back seat and climbed in behind them.

"So, what's your name, man?" Jerry asked.

"Chuck. Yours?"

"Jerry, and the funny looking lad driving is Mike. Where are you heading?"

"South. All the way to Florida. Can't stand this snow and

wind and shit, y'know? I got a gig in Tampa, a coffee house, *The House of Seven Sorrows.* I'm a musician." That explained the guitar case. "How about you two?

"Same as you, pal. Coming from Ohio, going to Florida. Clearwater to be exact. I don't think it's far from Tampa. My great-aunt has a place there. That's where we're staying."

"Damn! That's just across the bay from Tampa. This is cool," Chuck smiled. "One ride all the way. Mind if I smoke?"

Jerry and I glanced at each other. "Well, maybe we'll take you all the way. I mean if you don't get on our nerves," I said. "Go ahead and smoke. But, we have to have an agreement, here. If things get uncomfortable you got to bail, agreed?"

"Agreed. I won't get on your nerves, really. I can sleep back here and stay real quiet."

"Man, you can talk if you want." I couldn't get the man at HoJo's out of my mind. "I just meant, you know, weird. It's good to have some company other than my good buddy Jerry, here."

"Bite me, Malloy."

"So, you boys are from Ohio. I was worried some local would pick me up and I'd have to listen to 'nigger' this and 'nigger' that. Okay, here's my story, straight up," Chuck said, leaning forward and resting his arms on the back of the front seat. "See, I just got out of the hospital back there. In Lexington."

Oh, shit. "What was the problem?" Jerry demanded. No way we were going to be cooped up with someone just recovering from god knows what, maybe some weird contagion, for the rest of the trip. We still had two days and a night's travel ahead of us before we got to the beach. No way some bullshit disease would screw everything up.

Chuck hesitated and took another deep drag on his cigarette.

He let the smoke drift slowly from his nostrils. "Man, I sure missed a good smoke. They didn't allow it in there."

"Right, but what were you there for? Were you sick or something?" I let Jerry handle the interrogation.

"Yeah, well, I guess you could say that," Chuck slowly answered. "I was in the federal hospital where they send people with a drug, you know, situation, if they don't send you to prison. The hospital is like a prison, though. No bars on the windows or locked cells, but if you walk away you go to the federal slam and serve your full sentence with five years tacked on for escaping. When the judge sentences you, in New York anyway, where I'm from, if you're a junkie he offers you a choice. Jail or the hospital. I took the hospital. Three years, man. A real trip. The only thing that kept me from losing my shit completely was thinking about getting out and back on the circuit. It was weird, man, you have no idea. They were doing this thing on some of us called 'behavior modification' or some shit like that, and that was the scariest part because they said they were changing our thoughts, rearranging our thinking, disconnecting things in our heads so we wouldn't want dope anymore. They said it was a new idea and it was gonna help us. Bullshit, man. We were an experiment, a fucking experiment. Just like they always do to us." He frowned, his face tightening into anger. "Scared the shit outta me, man. I was afraid I'd forget my music, y'know? Maybe forget my name! Motherfuckers . . ."

Jerry missed Chuck's mood completely. "A real drug addict. Damn. I bet that was a bitch, right? Malloy is on his way, too." He jerked his thumb in my direction. "He's gonna wind up there someday, in that hospital. He steals his mother's diet pills! Swallows 'em like Lifesavers. Right, Mikey?"

"Fuck you. That's unreal, Chuck. Sounds like something from a movie. Do they do alcoholics, too? Like my buddy Jerry here. He'd inject booze if he could. Right into a vein. Drinking that nasty shit is too slow."

Chuck gave a both a quick look, as if he might have made a mistake getting into the car. Maybe it would've been better to stay in the cold, wait for the next car to stop. What kind of crazy shit were these two white boys into?

"Yeah, there's an alky ward there," Chuck continued. "Lotta screaming, too. People drying out, coming off heroin, cocaine, you name it. Some of 'em die right up in there. I'm telling you, the place is a nightmare. But, it was go there or the federal pen. No way I was going back to prison."

"*Back* to prison?"

"It was no big deal, man. Car theft a few years ago. When you have a monkey riding your ass, you gotta feed it or it will thoroughly beat the fuck out of you. That's what heroin does. A couple of years and I got out for good behavior. Then this last time they gave me a choice: hospital or back to the pen. That was an easy choice."

So, we had picked up a black ex-con, a former heroin addicted car thief who had had his thoughts "rearranged" during experiments in a federal hospital. Great. Was he really a musician? Was the guitar case empty or did it house a machine gun? Was he insane? Should I ask him to get out, get back on the side of the road? Freeze his ass to death?

Jerry changed the subject. "So, what kind of music do you play?"

Chuck smiled, "There's only one kind, man. The Blues." He moved his duffel bag and guitar around, trying to get comfortable. "You boys mind if I close my eyes for a minute?

I was awake all night in the train station pretending I was waiting for a ride."

Jerry turned back around. "Hey, go ahead. Get some Z's. There's a pillow back there somewhere." Within minutes, Chuck was slumped against his guitar case, asleep, his drooping head shifting from side to side as the road curved.

"Why did he have to pretend he was waiting on a ride?" Jerry half-whispered, as if I knew.

"Dunno, pal. Ask him when he wakes up. Maybe because they don't want people hanging around unless they've got a scheduled ticket."

"So, what do you think?" he asked. "We gonna take him all the way to Tampa?"

"Sure, why not? When he wakes up maybe he'll play some music."

Jerry was considering what taking our passenger all the way to Tampa meant. "Shit, there goes my bed, right? If he's back there the rest of the way. And what if we're stopped? No drivers' licenses and a colored guy in the back seat. In the South? Two white guys and a colored guy and a car with Ohio license plates? Damn!"

"Relax, Jer. What could possibly go wrong?" I swallowed another diet pill and felt the rush of chemical energy. I wanted to drive forever. *Zoom-zoom.*

Hours later, early afternoon, and we had crossed another state line. We were in Tennessee. The weather had changed. It was warm. The sunlight was dancing in the trees like ecstatic sprites, flashing into my eyes and momentarily blinding me every few hundred yards. The road was clear and dry, the sky was a soft blue, and the air rushing through the open windows smelled like Spring. Beautiful.

Chuck woke up from his nap, coughing like he was going to bring up a lung.

"Damn, I'm . . . sorry," he managed between gasps for air. "Too much . . . fresh air, I guess."

"Sounds like TB," Jerry volunteered. "You got TB?"

"I doubt it. Been locked in for three years. Just tired."

"Too noisy to sleep in the train station last night?" I asked.

"Naw, it was quiet in there. Hard to sit on those wooden benches all night, though. Couldn't lie down and no trains until early this morning." He paused. "Then I had to leave, get out on the street, before people started coming in."

"Why'd you have to leave so early? Couldn't you stay there until it got a little warmer out? You, know, wash up, brush your teeth?"

"We can't do that down here, man. There're rules. They catch us what they call 'loitering' and they'll put us out weeding tobacco for some dirt farmer. And, they'll keep a Negro doing that for as long as they want. Colored folk can disappear into shit like that. Just like slave times. So, I had to get outta there before someone realized I wasn't in there waiting for a train."

"Couldn't you just say you were cold? You had to come in to warm up a little?"

Chuck was looking at me through the rear-view mirror. "You boys don't know 'bout any of this stuff, do you. Look, it's different up north. They can run you off up there by insulting you or threatening to beat your ass, but you can't be put out on some damn farm to do slave labor. Laws? Shit, man, laws aren't for us. They're for white people. And, down here? We gotta keep moving or stay out of sight. Always been that way."

I tried to imagine living what Chuck was telling us about.

Afraid to nod off in a train station? What he was saying went way beyond the segregation we learned about in our history and government class.

We drove on. The miles were rolling by, now that the weather was clear and dry. I couldn't get over how quickly it had changed. Early this morning, snow and ice. Here it was late afternoon and it felt like a warm spring day. Really warm. We were coming up on another small Tennessee town and when I came around a bend in the road, tucked between two brick bungalows, there was a Dairy Queen.

"All right! Ice cream! I'm gonna stop. Anybody want one? Jer? How about you, Chuck?"

I pulled into the gravel parking lot. "You guys go ahead," Chuck said. "I'll duck down in the seat so no one can see me. No shit, now, with this Ohio car and you two white boys, well, you don't want these cracker-ass fools to see me. Might get awkward."

There it was again. The sort of racism I had only read about. It was scary as hell to realize all three of us might be in serious trouble if Chuck was seen in our car. And, it made me angry. But, in that moment, fuck it. I wanted an ice cream cone. Jerry and I got out of the car and walked to the order window. Did I want vanilla or chocolate? Chocolate. So, I went to the other window to order, the chocolate window. Jerry was getting vanilla so he stayed at the vanilla window. There we were, a couple of tired, hungry, road-weary delinquents, on our way to Florida waiting on our ice cream cones. The two middle-age white women inside started acting strange. They served Jerry but kept looking at me and whispering to each other. Looking and whispering. I couldn't understand why they wouldn't come over and take my order. All I wanted was a ten-cent chocolate ice cream cone. Was there a problem? Jerry walked back to the car and leaned against the hood, licking his vanilla ice cream cone, and watching whatever the fuck was going on. I was getting impatient. "Excuse me," I said through the closed service window. "Can I get a chocolate cone?" More looking and whispering. And, something new. Sneering. The women were sneering at me, that curled lip look that said you're an asshole. What the hell was going on? Jerry figured it out.

"Hey, man, You're at the wrong window."

"What wrong window? I want a chocolate cone, right? This window is for chocolate cones. Look at the goddam sign up there! It says . . . " *Oh, shit.* It said "*colored.*" Not as in chocolate ice cream. As in skin color.

I walked over to the proper window. "Can I get a ten cent chocolate cone, please?" I asked the woman standing nearest the window. She looked at me like I had just said, "Hi, can I get a piece of ass, please?"

She grabbed a cone, filled it with chocolate Dairy Queen, opened the window screen and pushed it out. "That'll be ten cents," she snarled. Christ, the other one was probably in back calling the local KKK chief. I could guess what she was saying.

"Hey, Lloyd? Yeah, it's Sara Mae. Lissen, there's a couple of fellers here looking to start trouble. One of 'em just tried to order at the colored window. What? No, he's white. Got Ohio license plates on their car, too. There's two of 'em. You might want to come over here and straighten things out. Might be some of those damn freedom riders. No, there's no bus. They're in a blue car with a rope tied on the front. One of those thick ropes. Yeah, that's what I was thinking, too. Okay, Lloyd. Hurry up. They look like trouble, for sure."

Jerry waved me over to the car. "C'mon. Let's get the hell

out of here. There might be a posse on the way over."

We got in the car. Chuck was lying down in the back seat laughing his ass off. "Damn," he said between spasms, "that's some funny shit! The chocolate, no wait, the *colored* ice cream window!" He was still laughing as I threw the gear shift into low, stomped the accelerator, and spun a barrage of gravel at the two bitches inside their glass ice cream shop.

Chapter 7

White Bears, Brown Rabbits

"Hey, Chuck," Jerry turned half around in the front seat. "Do you have a driver's license?" It was getting dark and I thought about pulling over and switching places with Chuck so he could drive and I could try to come down from what was beginning to feel like a Benzedrine overdose. My hands were shaking, my pulse was off the chart, and that powerful "I can do anything" feeling had been replaced with a sense of impending doom.

"Driver's license?" Chuck answered. "Not after being locked in for three years, no, I don't have one. Why?"

Jerry smiled and took another slug from his remaining half-bottle of Old Grandad. "Well, I was hoping you had one because we don't. Nope. No driver's license." He nodded in my direction, "My buddy here never got one and mine was suspended. Ain't that some shit? Rippin' through the South with no driver's licenses. *Yeeee-hawwwww* . . .! Drive on, my man!"

Chuck leaned forward and looked at both of us, first Jerry, then me. "You're kidding, right? No? Well, you two are taking one hell of a chance. But, no, I don't have one either."

Jerry laughed, "I'm not taking a chance. He is!" He jerked his hand towards me and whiskey sloshed out of the bottle and spilled on the front seat.

"Goddam, man!" I couldn't help yelling at him. The Dairy Queen episode had freaked me out and my amphetamine-induced paranoia was starting to get worse. "Now if we get stopped we're really in deep shit, dropping that cheap-ass whiskey all over the place. Smells like a fucking drunk tank in here!"

Chuck must have felt it was time for some music, something to break the tension that suddenly filled the car. He took his guitar out of the battered case and, after a quick tuning, started to play. "Anything you want to hear?" he asked us.

"Know any B.B. King?"

"Oh, yeah," and he launched into *B.B. Boogie.* He was good. Had the licks down as close to the way King would do it as anyone I've heard since. Then *Shake It Up And Go, 3 O'clock Blues, Every Day I Have The Blues.* It was our own rolling B.B. King concert. "He's my man. You dig him, too, right? But, you know what? All this Negro music is getting recorded by white musicians, white rock and roll, right? Like, Jerry Lee Lewis and Elvis and all these other white boys are making baskets of money off songs black singers never got paid for. It's our music, for sure, but who gives a shit. Black folk just don't get credit. For nothin' good. Pisses me off, it really does." He had stopped playing and was staring out the window. "Shit just never stops, man."

I had no idea what he meant. Rock and roll was just that. What connection did it have with what Chuck called "Negro music?" So, I asked him. "What do you mean Negro music and white boys stealing it? How did they steal it?"

Jerry had passed out and was leaning against the door. His wet, rattling snoring was getting louder. I reached over and shook his shoulder. What if I opened his door and pushed him out? No. Don't do that. Focus on driving.

Chuck paused before answering me. Then, "Long story, my man. See, it started with gospel slave songs, the blues did. Slaves made it up to ease the pain. When they were allowed to go to church they'd sing all these songs about the pain and sorrow they had to deal with. And in the churches they found the rhythm, the rockin' and rollin,' like this one old song that says, *'We been rockin' and rollin' in your arms, rockin' and rollin' in your arms, rockin' and rollin' in the arms of Moses.'* That's how it started. Church singin.' And before that were the slave ships that rocked and rolled when they were loaded up with Africans. And the ocean swells that caused so many of those brothers and sisters to get sea-sick and then get tossed overboard like garbage by the crews who got tired of hearing their wailing and screaming, got tired of the vomit and shit smell. And, the bodies, there were lots of bodies, can't forget those. The sharks would circle the ships waiting for more corpses. You wanna guess how many Africans died on their way here to work as slaves?"

How did we get to this horror story? The subject was B.B. King! The subject was rock and roll music! What was Chuck telling me? The drugs I had been swallowing became a pulsing spasm that was making me paranoid and sweaty. Chuck's story was going to unleash a scream if I didn't get a grip. Outside, rushing past in a dark blur of pine trees and caved-in shacks, I thought I saw horses galloping beside us in the darkness. No. It was just the shadows of trees and utility poles.

"Thrown overboard? In the middle of the ocean?? To drown?

65

Jesus Christ, Chuck. I didn't know about this, I never heard this before! We weren't taught about this! This isn't in our American History textbook. This is insane!" No, it wasn't insane at all. It was just another cover-up, another attempt to bury a singularly evil part of U.S. history that white Americans had created from an insatiable and untethered lust for money and power. This "Christian" nation had forced a race of people into slavery to get the labor they needed to build this new white empire. Slavery was just one obscenity among many, a collection of moral crimes committed so our "Manifest Destiny" could be realized. What a horrible fucking joke.

The incident at school right before Jerry and I left Toledo rushed back at me, vividly, not yet a buried memory, made even more intense by what Chuck was telling me. I saw it again. The effigy hanging in the oak tree, students wandering about under its silent violence, not knowing what to do or say, staring up at the thing, the sign around it's waist that said, "HOMECOMING QUEEN." Chuck leaned forward and rested his arms and chin on the back of the front seat.

"How many, Chuck? How many people died?" I asked. In the darkness I was trying to read the expression on his face as he laid out this murderous, violent history that I knew nothing about. What other pieces of the past were waiting for me to discover; bloody realities that would make me want to hide in disgust and shame. It was difficult to see his face in the cracked rear-view mirror but, from his tone of voice, I knew his expression would be blank, empty. There was nothing I could say, no question I could ask that wouldn't show my ignorance of a holocaust I knew nothing about.

"Hey, look, man, it's history, y'know? That shit happened a long time ago," he said. "You ever smoke reefer? You know,

Mary Jane? Weed?" The subject was being changed.

"Not yet. I'll do it someday, absolutely. I don't know where to get it in Toledo."

"Wanna try some?"

"You have marijuana with you? Right now?"

"I do, indeed," he answered. "And, no, I didn't have any when I was a lab rat in that fucking hospital. But, I made friends with a guy who served his time, got out, he lives right there in Lexington, and he brought me a lid the afternoon I was freed. White guy, too. How about that?" he grinned. "I'll roll one up."

He leaned back in the seat, opened his guitar case, and pulled out a large envelope. "Just take me a minute."

"Okay, but I've taken quite a few diet pills, Dexedrine, in the last day or two. It's really fucking me up right now. Things are a little out of focus, y'know? Will reefer make it worse?"

Chuck laughed. "Naw, it'll take the edge off. Meth is the one that'll really fuck you up, man. What's your dose?"

"Dose?"

"Yeah, how much are you doing?"

"I grabbed a handful of my mom's dirt pills before we left. I took quite a few, I think, but only to make this trip." I thought I'd feel better if I confessed. "But, man, I'm feeling weird as hell all of a sudden. I see light trails every time I move my head. What the fuck?"

Chuck leaned forward and held out the joint. "Have you eaten lately?"

"I don't think so." I couldn't remember. There was an ice cream cone at some point, does that count? "Does an ice cream cone count?" I took the joint.

Jerry sat up. "You fucked up, Mikey? Wha's happening? I

67

been telling you for years you're weird"

"I've only known you for two years. Thought you were asleep," I said.

"I was, until all this funny dope talk. I told you to take it easy with those caps. You think he'll have a heart attack, Chuck? That shit causes heart attacks, right?" he said with a big smile. That's my buddy Jerry. Funny guy. Yeah, well, that's all I needed to hear. Heart attack? Out here on this dark two-lane? Somewhere in the Tennessee backwoods surrounded by armed hillbillies? I could feel the panic building.

Chuck was laughing, too. "That is a possibility. Maybe a stroke!"

"Damn! No offense, Chuck, cuz I don't know you that well, but, fuck you, okay? You two are making this worse."

"Hey, I'll drive, Mikey," Jerry offered.

"In a pig's ass, you'll drive. You've had too much to drink." No way in hell I'd be in a car Jerry was driving, drunk or sober. He knew only two speeds: dead stop and speeding bullet.

"Here," Chuck said again. "Take this, fire it up, you'll feel a lot better." Jerry pulled out his lighter and held it near my face. The flame obliterated everything except the car's interior and the white lights dancing at the edge of my peripheral vision . "Here ya' go, Mikey. I want to see you get high."

I sucked in a thick drag of pungent smoke and felt it burn all the way down my throat and into my lungs. Pow! When I stopped coughing, Chuck said, "That usually happens to first time tokers. Do it again, this time slower when you inhale. Reefer's your friend. So, be gentle. Don't rush it."

So, this was marijuana. "Is that it?" I asked Chuck. "So, what's the big deal?" The joint – Chuck's word – looked exactly like the bottom of a penny sucker, the skinny white stick you held on to that always gets sticky. Over the next few seconds, I took another two or three puffs. High? Did I get high? Stoned? Hard to tell, except when I said, 'Is that it?' my voice came from back seat Mike, the one sitting on top of Chuck's duffel bag watching front seat Mike drive.

"How do you feel?" Chuck wanted to know. "It's got a little booster in it, something a few of us patients were given."

"Uh . . . booster?"

"It's okay. It won't mess you up. They used it on us. Found it one night when I was wandering the halls trying to find an unlocked door, some way to escape. I went into one of labs and found a flask of clear liquid and someone had written on the label, 'Exp. Only. Use only under Dr. Behr's direct supervision.' I poured a little into a bottle I found on one of the shelves and took it back to my room. I was really down that night, tired of all the shit I was dealing with just because I'd been caught selling a couple of grams. I didn't know what would happen if I took some, but everything was fucked up so I didn't really care. Anyway, I swallowed a little and a few minutes later started seeing all sorts of interesting patterns and colors and shit like that. It was so cool. And, I felt happy. No shit. Happy. So, I picked up my guitar and started playing music I seemed to know, but I'd never heard before, right? It was way strange. I should have written everything down but I didn't have a pencil. I have no idea where that music came from. So, not all reefer is as good as what you're smoking. Most of it will just make you a bit spacey, hungry, feeling like you've got to have a Hershey's with almonds. What you have there is different. But, it's cool. Won't hurt you a bit."

"Well, this is really . . . I don't know . . . warm and quiet. Yeah, that's it. All that constant chatter that goes on in your head, y'know? It's all stopped."

"Well, enjoy," Chuck offered. "I'm gonna get some sleep. Wake me if it gets weird."

Right. Wake him if it gets weird. The road was deserted. It must have been past midnight. I hadn't heard a sound from Jerry for what seemed like hours. Maybe it was hours. His head had fallen back against the window, his mouth open, his arms loose and laying on his thighs. He was snoring. I was trying to decide if I should wake him up, but no, let him sleep. While I was still looking at Jerry the first bear flashed by outside, sitting by the side of the road, holding a rabbit. I almost missed seeing it. The bear was white, the rabbit was brown and it had extra big ears. There was no reason to question it. The bear wasn't bothering anything, just staring straight ahead, a slight smile raising the corners of his snout. The rabbit seemed content to sit where it was. Then the second bear flashed by, and the third. Each was holding a rabbit, it's claws wrapped around the rabbit's midsection. More bears flew by. I tried to count them, but they were going by too quickly. They were literally zipping past me, one after the other.

I shouted for Chuck to wake up. I needed someone to tell me if the bears and the rabbits were moving or sitting still. But, the shout was all in my head. There was no sound no matter how loud I thought I was yelling. I glanced down at the speedometer. It read 25 miles per hour. But, how could that be? The black trees alongside the road were fluid blurs, ripping by as fast as the bears and rabbits. We had to be going 80 or 90 miles an hour. No, the speedometer showed 25.

Things were getting seriously bat-shit crazy. I kept glancing at the speedometer as I pushed the gas pedal to the floor. The Olds seemed to leap ahead. Forty, fifty, sixty miles an hour, faster and faster until the bears were nothing but a white smear against the night, a washed-out contrast to the inky shadows rolling by in the deep darkness.

I had to stop the car, see if the bears were real, get a grip on whatever the hell was happening. I slowed down. A few hundred feet ahead there was a clearing, a road-side rest area. In the shadows, I could see a picnic table and some sort of structure. Perfect. I pulled in to this tiny oasis and stopped the car. There were no bears. No rabbits. Just deep and profound silence. I turned to wake them up, but Jerry and Chuck were not in the car. They had vanished. No, not vanished. Ridiculous. I must have let them out to take a piss at some point. Did I drive off and leave them? When did I do that? We hadn't come through a town or passed a truck stop. How did they get out of the car?

I reached into the glove box for the flashlight and got out of the car. There was no use worrying about where they were. They weren't here. They'd come back.

I walked over to the picnic bench, sat down and moved the flashlight's beam slowly around the rest area. There was trash and debris scattered under the table, bits of bread, chicken bones, a shredded sandal. The silence gave way to night noises coming from the woods, small sounds, chirps, wings beating against the night, tree frogs, a hungry owl. The highway I had just left was empty. I couldn't remember seeing or passing any other cars. Maybe I was the first person to use it. Or the last.

Then, under the forest sounds, I could hear something different; shuffling, low murmuring, dead leaves crunching and twigs snapping, as though people were moving through the brush. I turned and aimed the flashlight beam into the darkness.

Chapter 8

The Freedom Train

Something was moving through the woods. In the fragmented light I saw what appeared to be people, walking in a single file, the shapes broken by the shadows in the thick underbrush. All at once they stopped, frozen in the darkness that was now diffused by my flashlight, not moving. There was silence. The night sounds had stopped.

Then, a man's voice from the shadows, deep, slow and hesitant: "Hullo . . .is . . . you him? Is you de conductor . . . we s'posed to meet? Is you dat man?"

"What . . .? Who are you?" My voice was dry and weak. I followed the beam of light into a small clearing where the shadows morphed into people. There must have been twenty of them huddled together, standing silently. They were barefoot and dressed in muddy rags that hung from their dark, skeletal bodies. Their heads were bowed, they were silent. Out of the darkness, a tall man slowly approached me, two or three hesitant steps at a time. He seemed to be the leader. His hands were large and knotted and hung at his sides. His face was half-covered with a white beard that reached to the middle of his chest, clotted with brambles and clumps of dirt. He asked again, slowly, hesitantly.

"Is you . . . da man we sposed' to meet? Is you dat . . . conductor man?"

"Conductor?" I replied. "Like on a train?"

"Yas'suh, like dat. Dat freedom train. Is you who we s'posed to meet out heah? Dey gimme dis heah paper, suh, but I cain't read none of it, nawsuh. Is we neah dis place? Dis train place?" He thrust a damp, crumpled paper toward me. It was a map of sorts, a faint drawing of a river? A forest? A path leading to some sort of small building, a house, a shed? A large dark X was drawn through the building, if that's what it was. "Kin you tell me 'bout dis, suh? Is dis place roun' heah, suh?" He pointed at the X.

"I don't know. I mean, I don't know what this is all about? Who are you folks?" Fear slid across his face.

"You ain't him? Oh, Lawd. Please, now, suh, jest leave us be, let us go on." His voice had an edge of panic, the words tumbling out now, difficult to understand. "We have chirren in here. We not lookin' to be a trouble, sho' 'nuff. Aw, please, suh, we got to keep movin'. We got to move on. Got to find dat conductor. Don' tek us back dere, suh, please." He pointed into the dark woods behind him. A muffled cry, cut short, came from the middle of the line. "Dese heah babies dey be tired and hungry. Please, now, suh, jest let us go on."

Babies in this deep forest? "Mister, shouldn't these kids be home this late at night?" I asked, trying to sound rational, but my chest was tightening, my heart beating faster. I wanted to run back to the car. I started to turn . . .

The bearded man suddenly dropped to his knees, his hands clasped and raised in front of him, as though he were praying to me. Absolute panic choked his words.

"Please, suh . . . don' take us back . . . dere."

What the fuck?

"Please, suh. Mastuh' Bannon will bile us . . . like he done de others. He will, sho' 'nuff. He say any niggahs dat run away gon' be biled and fed to dem hogs. Please suh!"

He leaned away from the circle of light as though it would burn him. "Dat torch, suh, please don' let it harm the chirren. Please don' burn 'em. Dey jest babies . . ."

"Torch? This is no torch. It's just a flashlight, mister," I said. "It can't hurt the kids. Or anybody. It's batteries. That's what's making the light." I was explaining a flashlight? "What is this? Who are you people? Are you lost? What do you mean someone's going to 'bile' you? I don't know that word, 'bile.'" The others stayed silent and unmoving. The only sound was the unhinged conversation between the tall man and me, and the night-whispers that had resumed pulsating in the woods.

The tall man stood and, head down, slowly answered. "That white man," he looked back into the woods, "whut owns the place back dere, we be his. He's da one who say he'll bile us, cook us like biled yams. And den he feed us to da pigs." His head dropped to his chest. "Thet's whut he done to da others, screaming and hollerin' and bein' pushed into thet bilin' pot in back da big house where dey took 'em after dey cotched dem hidin' in da' swamp." As he described this horror his voice rose and fell. "Da' whole fambly, all dem, one after tha' other, screamin' and beggin' and shoutin' fo' Jesus and thet white man jus' pushin' dem under the bilin' water, one at a time wid' a long stick, the chirren fust den dey's momma and den dey's daddy and dey's momma an' daddy be watchin' dey's chirren git cooked like yams and screamin' such as nevah' bin heard, an' den made dem othah' niggas' take sticks and lift da' bodies out da water like biled meat an' dat smell and put 'em in da wagon and den ovah to da place dey keeps da pigs and da pigs be gittin' all runnin' aroun' and snortin' *cuz dey knew it wuz gittin' time to eat . . .*" He stopped. His breathing was heavy and labored. His hands had curled into fists. Tears rolled down his face. The horror of what he was saying filled the small clearing and made it stink of boiled meat. I stared at him . . . .Jesus Fucking Christ! *Jesus Bleeding Fucking Christ!* The tall man's words, his talk of people being boiled alive, was pure horror. It was impossible not to see the agony he was describing, impossible not to hear the screams. This hysterical old man can't be real. None of this is real. I'm asleep in the car. I felt disoriented, nauseous, unable to understand what was happening. It *must* be a dream. But the ground felt solid under my feet. I could hear the night sounds. I could smell my own sweat. Nothing was familiar. Just the dark woods and the faded people and the tall man and me. I tried again, trying to force an outline of reality, trying to banish the images of people being boiled alive.

"Who are you? Are you lost? Why are you out here in the middle of the night?" After a moment he answered. His voice was weak, exhausted.

"Suh, I done tole you. I truly did. Tole you jest now, suh. We tryin to git to dat conductor and de railroad, the one dey be talkin' 'bout. Iffn we don' go we gon' die an' no one evah know we lived. Please, suh, we got to git to thet railroad, thet one dats in de ground. We don' mean no trouble, suh, we jest got to go on."

"Look, mister, I have no idea what you're talking about. I know you need help. Do you want me to try to find a phone and call the Sheriff?"

"*Oh, Lawd no!* NO, suh, don' hollah fo' a Sheriff." Again, he had dropped to his knees, his hands clasped and raised to the night sky. "We come dis far an' nobody done heard us or seen us til you be standin' there. Now, we hopin' even tho' you be a white man you gon' hep us. We jest need git to dat train, suh, and to dat conductor. An' we think it's ovah dis way heah'." He pointed again into the forest, the opposite direction from where I'd first seen them. "Please suh."

His eyes shone black in the fading flashlight beam. "Mister, I'm just traveling through this area. I'm trying to get to Florida. I don't know about a train except there's a station back in Lexington and that's a long way from here. If there's a train station around here, I have no idea. And, what do you mean it's 'in the ground?'"

"Suh, dats whut I knows 'bout it. In de groun'. Dat's how niggahs 'scape. On dat train. We got to find it, suh."

And then I understood what the tall man was trying to tell me. He was looking for the Underground Railroad, the one I had read about in our American History class. The slaves' road to freedom in the 1800s. The route north all the way to Canada, if they made it. But, now? This was now! There were no slaves. This was 1959 not 1859. I started to tell him there was no railroad. There never was. It was metaphor, an escape route, yes, but no train. It was never real. You couldn't ride on it.

He raised his head, panic rippled across his face. "Suh, iffen you not de conductor. . ."

His voice trailed off. He got slowly to his feet. I could see, in the dim circle of light, the pain in every movement, as though his bones had been broken and healed and broken again.

"We gon' go den, suh, iffen you don' know nuffin' 'bout it. I got to take deese folks on to freedom. Y'all come on, now. Dis man ain't him, ain't dat conductor. We got to keep walkin'. Y'all come on, dis man ain't gon' hurt us, naw he ain't gon' hurt us sho' 'nuff."

They again formed a single line, the tall man at the front. He turned to me. "Now, please, suh, don' let dem know we wuz dis way. Make lak you nevah done seen us, suh. That's all I be askin' of you."

"Okay. I can do that," I answered, sounding totally nonsensical. But, what else could I say to these shades and this tall man who was leading them? There was nothing. Absolutely nothing. I stood there as they faded into the forest, moving silently, like ghosts. The darkness enveloped them, and they were gone.

It was suddenly silent. No chirping tree frogs, no wind moving the bare tree branches, no night raptors or bats moving through the air, hunting. I didn't feel like moving. I felt as though I *shouldn't* move, that standing there motionless was the safest thing I could do. Safe. From what? Something had been disturbed by their presence, something that could bring incredible chaos if let loose.

The flashlight was getting dimmer. *Dammit!* These were new batteries! The circle of light went to black and the shadows became threatening, sinister. I turned and in near-panic ran in the direction I had come, back through the brush, the knotted kudzu and tangled privet causing me to stumble, the vines scraping at my face, tearing at my clothing.

Where was the road? Had I come this far when I left the car? There was no path to follow, just darkness. I slammed into a low-hanging branch. A hot pain arched across my forehead.

I could feel a trickle of blood dripping into my eye. I wiped it away with my sleeve.

This had to stop. I had to get a grip, walk slowly, find the road and the car. Jerry and Chuck must still be sleeping, or they would have called out or come looking for me. I had to get far away from all that had happened, even though I knew it couldn't have been real. It couldn't have been.

I pushed the tall man's damp, balled up piece of paper, crumpled in my fist, deep into my jeans pocket.

Chapter 9

Secrets

I wanted to yell for Jerry or Chuck. I was lost, turned around. I sucked in a lung-full of air, a bellowing shout building in my chest. Then a piercing shaft of scattered light and the sound of a car's engine cut through the underbrush. Headlights! Not twenty-five yards in front of me. I pushed through the last tangle of bushes and chest-high undergrowth (was it this thick when I walked into these woods?) and back into the clearing where I had left the car. I could see red tail-lights disappearing down the road, a midnight traveler swallowed by the night's swirling mystery.

Thank god the Olds was where I'd left it. I walked up to the driver's side and opened the door. The dome light, dim and spidery, nonetheless made it clear: no Chuck, no Jerry. I reached inside, grabbed a paper towel lying on the seat, and wiped the trickle of blood from my forehead.

I stepped back and again was about to shout just as Jerry came from behind the shed zipping up his fly. "Damn, man! Where the fuck *were* you? You had us worried. We couldn't figure out where you'd gone, out here on this scary-ass road.

So, I took a piss. We were about to come looking for you. Where were you?" Good question.

"In the woods, Jer. Back there." I pointed to the black forest. "No big deal."

Chuck walked out of the darkness behind me carrying a broken tree limb. He held it aloft, like a lance. "Yeah, Rescue Unit Number One was about to enter the forest and save you from whatever night-spook grabbed you away. And, I got this monster-spearing branch just in case it was the Klan or some such shit. Seriously, man, we were getting worried."

"Sorry, guys. Nature calls, right?" There was no way in hell I was going to tell them what had happened. The tall man? The terrified women and children? Slaves? *The Underground Railroad?!* Maybe after I had a chance to talk with someone (a minister? a psychiatrist? a medium?) who could sort it all out and explain to me what I had walked into. I still felt out of balance, disconnected, as though I had been somewhere far away from this roadside rest stop. I had to clear my head, get back – if that's the right term – to this reality. I was on my way to Florida with two other people; my good friend Jerry from Toledo, and a hitch-hiker we had picked up in Kentucky named Chuck. Right now, that's all I needed to know.

"We thought we heard you talking with someone out there," Jerry said, nodding toward the forest. "Really. Sounded like you were having quite a discussion. All loud and shit. And what happened to your forehead? You walk into a tree?"

"Must have, Jer," I answered, trying to sound both casual and dismissive. "It's dark out there. And who in the hell would I have been talking to in the middle of the night, in some strange woods? Look, I was taking a dump, okay?" Casual and dismissive weren't working. I could hear the tension in my voice.

"Hey, no problem, Mikey. Didn't mean to pull your chain there, dude."

I had to change the direction of this conversation, quickly. "Hey, let's just get back on the road, okay? We still have Georgia to deal with."

I slid behind the wheel, Chuck got in front, and Jerry pushed aside the bags and suitcases and stretched out in the back. "Time to get back to my beauty sleep, boys, after all this interruption," he said. "Gotta be rested up for all those Southern beach bunnies just waiting for me to bring relief and joy to their barren and frustrated sex lives." His voice got louder, like a country preacher's. "I am their salvation, I am their *redemption!* I shall free them from all that bottled up nastiness their parents told them to ignore or they'd go to Hell! I *am* the man! I am the one they were warned about! Take a deep breath and uncross your legs, girls. *The Man is on the way! Yessss!"* Jerry was as full of shit as a Christmas goose. I glanced at Chuck who was either stifling a laugh or about to gag. With his hand over his mouth, I couldn't tell which.

Within minutes Jerry was asleep. Again.

I drove on in silence, trying to think through what had happened in the woods. It was a wasted effort. There was no rational explanation. Either it happened as I experienced it, or it was a hallucination, a waking dream. I wanted to talk with Chuck since he was older than me and certainly more experienced – at least that was my perception of him. He lived in New York City; he had been to prison; he had used drugs; he was a musician. And he was a Negro, like the . . . people . . . I had come across in the forest. He had to know things I didn't. I glanced over at him.

"So, Chuck . . ."

"Yeah . . . what's up?" He turned to face me, his forearm resting on the back of the seat.

"Uh . . . you've been around, right? You know . . . done things, seen things."

He chuckled. "Yeah, you could say that. No doubt."

"So, what's the weirdest thing you've ever experienced? The strangest? Like, something that had no explanation in . . . well, in the real world?"

"Man, that's some kinda question." He was silent for a moment. Then, "The weirdest thing? Hard to say. There's been so much. I could tell you stories that you wouldn't believe, scare the hell outta you. Make you sick. Things white folks couldn't possibly relate to. Why? Why do you ask?"

"Oh, I dunno." I couldn't tell him the real reason. I wondered if I'd be able to tell anyone, ever? "Just curious. Just making conversation."

"Weirdest? Is that what you want to know? Well . . ." He hesitated before going on, staring into the Southern darkness rushing past us. "There's been a lot of stuff, my friend. No offense but trying to tell a white person what it's like to be a Negro in America – and 'weird' doesn't get it - is a waste of time. Y'all wouldn't believe some of the shit we've had to deal with. But it's been a real trip so far, trust me on that. Inside our community we survive; outside, it's a nightmare."

"I can only imagine," I answered. I knew I probably sounded like a typical, unknowing white American. But, surely, Chuck knew that I knew something, a little, about the endless horror black people dealt with and had been dealing with for centuries. I was trying to manipulate the conversation, to get the information I wanted even though I wasn't certain what that might

83

be. "But, how about crazy shit . . . you know, stuff you couldn't explain, like maybe supernatural . . . anything like that ever happen to you?"

He was looking at me intently, the kind of look you can *feel* in the space between your face and the other person's eyes.

"'Supernatural'? Like ghosts and haints?" We were getting close to what I wanted to hear.

"Sure," I answered. "Ghosts and . . . what's *'haints'*?"

"You say 'haunts'. We say 'haints'. Well, a little history. The first thing you must understand, is where black folk come from: Africa. The Dark Continent, right? And your tribe comes from Europe where, back in the day, let's be real, hundreds of thousands of women, maybe millions, were burned to death, right? All because they knew about how to heal people when they were sick. Man, that's some crazy shit right there."

For real. When we studied this part of Medieval history in school, most of us couldn't believe it. Burning people at the stake? Killing them because they knew things the priests would not accept? But that was the power of the Church and if whatever it was didn't bow to the Church and the priesthood, it deserved to die; it *had* to die.

"But, see, in Africa," Chuck continued, "the people didn't do that. Those village women didn't know a damn thing about medicine, but they knew certain ways to heal folks who were hurting. And, they were honored for it because when you live in the jungle, man, there's a million things to fuck you up. Snakes and wild animals and poisonous spiders, all sorts of ways to make you sick or outright kill your ass.

"So, these women in the villages used herbs from the jungle and they did these strange-ass dances and chanting and blowing smoke at sick folks. My grandma told me all about

84

this because she wanted to make sure I knew about where my people came from and our culture back before it was destroyed by the slavers. And when these healing women – grandma calls them *sangoma* - when they wound up as slaves on the plantations in the so-called 'New World' they tried to keep doing what they had done in Africa. But she says it was harder because the *sangoma* ladies couldn't find the herbs and plants they used if Africa. But they kept on. They always kept on. They figured out how to use the new plants and what sort of the new herbs to give people. They wouldn't quit."

Chuck reached into his jacket pocket and took out a cigarette. The flare from his lighter gave his face the appearance of carved ebony. He stared out the window at the passing darkness. I stayed silent for a moment, not knowing what to say. I knew his telling this story had to be painful. I knew it but I couldn't feel it the way Chuck obviously did. Unlike his ancestors, my grandparents came to the "New World" freely, and not in the filthy hold of a slave ship stuffed with the dead and rotting as well as the barely living.

After a long silence I decided to ask, "So, they came to the new world and wouldn't quit. What happened then? Are there still these *sangomas* around? Do you know one?"

He turned to look at me and started chuckling. "Do I know one? Well, here's how it is: In the neighborhood, man, in just about every black ghetto neighborhood you'll find them. Yeah, they're still around. A whole new group."

I tried to imagine what one of these women must look like in modern, 1959 America.

"Now, we call them Root Ladies. You ever hear of Root Ladies?"

"No. What's a Root Lady?"

"Okay," he said. "You picked me up in the middle of a snowstorm in a place a nigger like me could've been lynched. For sport. So, I'm gonna tell you some Negro secrets. Like about the Root Lady. "

"I thought that word, nigger, was the one colored people hated. Why do you use it?"

"When whites use it, yeah, we hate it. But when we use it, that ugly power is gone. We say it to prove it can't hurt us. But, you wanna know about the Root Ladies, right?" I did.

I saw the oil indicator light on the dash was starting to flicker, a sign that I had to soon stop and pour in another couple of quarts to satisfy the Olds' insatiable thirst. I decided to keep driving. I didn't want to interrupt Chuck's story of the Root Ladies.

"Well, it's like this," he began. "In every neighborhood in every city in the country, and that's no exaggeration, whether it's in the North or the South, there'll be at least one woman, sometimes two, who you go see if you have something wrong, something you want fixed, or changed. You know, a stomach ache, the shakes, high blood, sugar, shit like that. Now, this woman is not someone you'd see on the street and think, 'that there is a medicine woman.' In fact, most of the Root Ladies are fat, old, dress like they're homeless, and just generally nasty-looking. I don't know why, but that's what they look like. Except on Sundays when they dress up for church. Maybe it's a disguise, like, back in the slave days to keep the Master from being able to single out these women, make them stop helping folks who were property, not people. Whatever.

"Anyway, she just looks like hell, and around her waist she'll have a rope or an old belt she found in the white folks' trash and hanging off that belt on her side would be a small bag. It's

86

either leather or cloth and it has all sorts of bulges and lumps in it that makes it thump against her hip when she walks, and she walks really slow because she's old and not in a hurry anyway. Inside the bag . . ."

"Roots?" I couldn't help it.

"Boy, you're jumpin' ahead of me, here. Yeah. Roots. All kinds of roots that she gets from the nearest empty lot or nearby woods. You'd be surprised what she can find in an empty lot. But also, all sorts of other, smaller bags with powders and dead insects, maybe spiders, and ground up god-knows-what. And a knife. Root Lady always carries a knife. Sometimes a few stones, sparkly crystals and black stones she gets from a river or creek, and maybe small, dried up dead snake parts. And, little vials like the ones you see behind the counter in a drug store. The vials have colored liquids in them, and Root Lady never tells what those liquids are. She also carries slips of paper with words written in the old languages of Africa that she uses to cast spells and conjure."

"Conjure what?"

Chuck smiled. "Whatever's necessary. Mostly, good energy she uses to drive demons *away* not call them up. The Root Lady is no fool."

Spells, demons, potions, incantations. I was getting a hell of a lot more from Chuck than I expected. "So, why didn't these Root Ladies use their power, their spells, to get free of the slave masters? Maybe even send a demon to tear them to pieces? And, why not now? I mean, colored people are still being treated like shit, right?" Again, he paused before answering.

"Seems obvious, doesn't it. Someone puttin' the torture on her why not strike out, make it stop, even if it means killing

87

somebody. The problem is, the Root Ladies are healers. Asking a Root Lady to do something ugly to someone would be like asking a doctor to *make* someone's appendix rupture. When they're taught how to heal, they are also told never to do harm. And, they never do, or they'll lose their power."

I thought of my neighborhood in Toledo and the black families moving in from the South, looking for work, a home, decent schools. I wondered how many of the old ladies, the grandmas who came with the families, were Root Ladies.

The flickering oil indicator light had stopped flickering and was now solid red. Time to stop and dump in another quart or two. I pulled to the side of the road, set the emergency break, and stepped out. It was then I saw the car that must have been following us with its headlights off. It had pulled off the road right behind us.

Suddenly, the road was lit up with dark crimson from the flashing light on the car's roof.

The police.

I could hear the sharp intake of Chuck's breath. Jerry jerked up in the back seat, startled awake by the red light that flooded the Olds from every direction. The car door opened and out stepped a man who must have weighed three-hundred pounds. He turned on the headlights and slowly walked toward us, his bulk outlined by the lights behind him.

"So, what're you boys up to this late at night?" he drawled. "Let me see some identification and don't none of y'all move too quick, y'hear?"

Chapter 10

Jail

There are valid reasons why certain stereotypes exist. They're drawn from examples that are constant enough to create the stereotype. So it was with small town Southern sheriffs in 1950s America. Big bellied, hair cut short and high around the ears, the thin remains on top plastered down with Wildroot Crème Oil, cheek bulging with a fist-size lump of chewing tobacco, a holstered .44 caliber hand gun with a long barrel that added to its intimidation factor, khaki pants held up with a wide brass-buckled belt, open collar white shirt, a supporter of the local Klavern, a Deacon at the Southern Baptist church, a God-fearing Christian, and, absolutely convinced the South would have won The War of Northern Aggression if General Lee hadn't run out of men at the battle of Appomattox Court House.

And, here he stood – The Small-Town Southern Sheriff - in the glare of his headlights and the clicking red light on top of his squad car, swinging round and round, throwing a circling blood-red glow from the road to the woods to the road to the woods . . .

"Now, I want y'all to do what I tell you and you won't be in any more trouble than you are already. 'Course, that's probably gonna be a bunch." He came closer to the driver's side of the Olds and peered inside. "You the driver, boy?" he asked me, his tobacco breath forcing me to stifle an almost overwhelming urge to gag.

"Yes, sir, I am, sir," I answered.

He aimed his flashlight inside the car. "And, who we got inside here? Well, looky here! I done found me a nigger! Lordy, this is my lucky night, sho' 'nuff. And, we got another white boy in here, too? My, my. I wonder what y'all are doin so far from home. Shoot, I bet it's sumthin' ugly."

He hadn't asked for my non-existent driver's license. So far, so good.

"Now, you," he pointed the beam into my face, "lemme see your license right quick."

Shit.

"Well, sir, it's like this . . ." I started to answer.

"They do give out driver's licenses up in Ohio, right? That's where y'all are from, ain't that right? Says so on the plate on the rear of your car. You gonna show me your license, boy? Or are you hopin' I'm just gonna git tired of askin' and drive off and that's the end of it?" He leaned into the road and spit out a mouthful of tobacco juice and coagulated spit.

"I don't have one, sir."

"You don't have one." Another stream of juice landed, this one on the white line, staining it forever.

"No, sir. I didn't get one yet."

"Well, then, Ohio, that raises a question. Why are you driving through my county late at night with a nigger in yore car and no driver's license? Can you give me an answer right quick?" Jerry leaned over and looked up at the Sheriff. "Sir, he's a good driver. Just 'cause he doesn't have a license don't mean a thing." Jerry was trying to be helpful.

"Boy, sit yore ass back in there and shut your mouth, right quick now." Jerry sat back and shut his mouth. Right quick.

"Well, looks here like I'm gonna have to take y'all down to the jail. No license, Ohio plate on your car, and two white boys and a nigger sneakin' around my county at 3:00 o'clock in the morning. Looks like we got a whole bunch of crimes happenin' here. Now, y'all follow me into town and don't even think about tryin' to drive off. That'd be fleeing a crime scene and then we got even more trouble. Understand?"

"Yes, sir," was all I could choke out. I felt the urge to gag again even though shit-breath was walking back to his car. He turned off the flashing red light and eased onto the highway in front of us. Then both of us made a looping U-turn and off we went to his jail.

Chuck quickly cranked down the one rear window that worked and threw something into the darkness alongside the road. "Christ, that was lucky! I thought he was gonna tell us to get out and put our hands on the roof and then the pat-down. That's the way it's usually done. *This* dumb ass wasn't thinking. We coulda' been carrying guns, coulda' shot the fucker. If he had found the reefer in my duffel, *damn* . . . hey, let me out and I'll take off. This fat-fuck sheriff has a thing for colored folk, no question. Just pull over and I'm gone. Seriously. I've been caught in enemy territory and if that ol' boy ain't in the Klan I'm not in deep shit, and believe me, I know deep shit when I'm in it." He was already pulling his duffel bag and guitar together. "For real, pal, I gotta go!"

"I can't Chuck. If I stop and let you out Jerry and I'll wind up on a chain gang and they might hang your ass when they catch you. And you know they'll catch you, right?"

"Man, this is some serious shit. I don't think you realize how serious." Chuck was getting agitated.

Jerry leaned into the back seat. "Hey, they wouldn't do anything to you, Chuck. There's two witnesses here. Us."

"How long do you think your 'two witnesses' will be around to witness anything if these crackers decide to have a little fun with the nigger? Huh?"

I had an idea. "Wait. Chuck did they give you an I.D. card at the drug rehab place? The Federal Hospital?"

"Yeah. So?"

"Do you still have it?"

"What difference does that make?"

"Well, I've read that when the Feds get involved with these local Southern cops, the good ol' boys aren't quite so hostile. The last thing they want is their crappy-ass county overrun with FBI agents stirring up all sorts of shit. So, if you still have your ID card with all the government stuff on it, maybe it'll confuse this jerk and he'll let us go. He might look at it and think you're some sort of agent. Does it say inmate on it?"

"You're crazy, man," Chuck answered as he dug into the duffel looking for his prison ID card. "Here it is, sweet Jesus. Turn on the dome light."

Chuck studied the card. "All right! It doesn't say inmate at all. Just my name and photo and it was issued by the Federal Government in Washington by God DC!"

"Then let's try it. It's the only possible way out of this, right?"

"Mikey," Jerry chimed in, "you're a genius. He's a genius, isn't he Chuck? Hey, you got an extra Kool? I'm out."

The city limits sign said, "Welcome to Horse Creek Crossing Home Of The 1956 Robert E. Lee High School State Champion Class A Football All-Stars The Mighty Rebels!" Under all that bullshit, in smaller type, "Population 17,000. The Lions' Club meets Wednesday 10AM Sharp at Lucille's Stop N Eat. We arrest speeders. Drive slow and you won't go to jail."

Yeah, this was the South for sure.

We made a couple of turns off Main Street and pulled in behind the Sheriff in the City Hall/County Jail gravel parking lot. Shit breath hoisted himself out of his squad car and waddled over to us.

"Wal, that was right smart of you boys, not tryin' to flee." Another stream of tobacco juice arched into the night. "Now, y'all git out of that car and follow me inside. Leave your stuff in the car. You won't be needing it for a while." That last had an ominous sound to it and Chuck poked me in the back as if to say, "See man, I told you!"

We walked into a brightly lit room that had a desk, a straight-back chair, a couple of filing cabinets, and a wooden bench that must have come from a church. Or maybe a funeral home. Nailed to one of the walls was a bulletin board covered with local announcements: upcoming church socials, garden club meetings, next month's scheduled Klan rallies, the Southern small-town gatherings that were the glue that held everything together and guaranteed order. On the desk, an oversize wooden plaque with gold embossed letters: Sheriff Roscoe P. Staunton.

Roscoe?

"Now you boys set over there on that bench. And you," he pointed to Chuck, "you come with me."

"Where you taking me?" Chuck asked. "I'd rather stay here

with these guys." His hands were shaking.

"Boy, I said come with me. Ain't gonna hang you. Ha-ha-ha! Yore ass is going into a cell back here. Ain't gonna take no chance of you runnin' out the door. I know 'bout you niggers."

Jerry stood up. "Your Honor, we'll keep an eye on him. He's not going anywhere. Honest. But we'd like to stay together. You know, sitting out here in your friendly office."

Sheriff Asshole turned to Jerry. "You better sit yore ass down, son. And, shut up. Yore gonna talk yourself into one of my cells you keep shootin' off yore mouth. Sit!"

Jerry sat.

My turn. "Sir, honest, we'd like to stay together here. We're new in town, actually just passing through, don't know a soul, and we're on our way to see his (I pointed to Jerry) great-aunt in Florida. She's a Christian." I was talking too fast.

Sheriff Asshole took Chuck by the collar and walked him over to Jerry and me. "Just passin' through, huh? Maybe not. Maybe yore gonna be here for a while. Won't know that til the judge comes in in the morning." He looked at the clock over the desk. "'Bout three hours from now. Meantime, you boys shut up and jest sit there. Next time you talk, 'less I talk to you, you'll be in back with yore nigger friend. Do you understand?" His eyes had narrowed and a vein in his neck was throbbing.

"Yes sir," I said. "For sure we understand, right Jer?"

"Yeah, I understand. I really do."

Sheriff Asshole turned, pushing Chuck ahead of him and the two of them disappeared behind a door that said "Jail." We listened as their footsteps faded.

"Jesus Christ!" Jerry whispered. "What are we gonna do?"

"I don't know. But, when that fat fuck comes back don't say anything, okay? We gotta figure this out. This is scaring the hell out of me, Jer. I've read about people from up North just disappearing down here. They arrest somebody and that's it. They're gone!"

The Sheriff came back and sat down behind the desk. He folded his hands, placed them on his bulging gut and leaned back in his chair. From under his desk he pulled out a rusted can that in a different life must have contained tomatoes or beans or maybe okra. Now, it was his spit can. He spit a glob of brown saliva into the can. "Now, where you boys from in Ohio?"

We blurted out, "Toledo." Jerry added, "Where they make glass! We're the glass capital of the world, sir. I bet the glass in the windows here in your office is from Toledo, right Mike?"

"Oh, yeah, sure. I bet it is." I wanted Jerry to shut the fuck up. This sheriff was a trickster, for sure, and anything we said would probably be presented as evidence we were Yankee troublemakers when the judge showed up.

But, ol' Jerry kept right on. "Most of the glass goes into new cars, you know windshields and rear view mirrors and stuff like that. It's good glass, too. Toledo makes the best glass ever! The best, right, Mike?"

I wanted to punch him.

"I don't wanna hear any more about yore glass, boy. What is your name, both of you?" Brown spit.

"Mike."

"Jerry. And, that's Chuck you took away . . ."

Sheriff Asshole leaned forward. "Now, I want the truth. You lie to me and yore mamas will never hear from you again. You hear me?"

We both nodded. I wanted to tell Silvia I was sorry for taking her diet pills and apologize for any pain I had caused her while

95

I was growing up and assure her I'd always love her even if this Sheriff had me killed. Jerry looked like he knew a beating was coming.

"What are you two Yankee boys doing in the middle of the night in my county? I asked you once, I better get an answer. Are you two and that nigger back there Communists? Agitators? Y'all down here to register our niggers to vote?"

Before we could plead our denials, the door that led to the Jail swung open slowly. An old black woman pushing a wash bucket and mop started to enter.

"Aw, I'm sorry, Sheriff! Honest I am! Din't know you was talking with folks. I'll come back later."

"Go ahead and come in here, Maylene. This floor looks like hogs been fuckin' in here. Just clean around these Yankee boys. They just got arrested and none of that concerns you."

"Yessuh, Sheriff. All right, then. I'll just get a bucket of clean water and be right back, suh. Thank you, suh."

Sheriff Spit turned back to Jerry and me. "Now, here's how it's gonna be. Judge Sessions don't get to the courthouse yonder 'til eight o'clock. That's when he starts his court." He pulled out his pocket watch. "And 'cordin to what it says here that'll be in three, four hours. You boys can sit right here and wait real quiet like, or I can put you in back with your nigger."

Jerry raised his head and looked at the Sheriff. "Sir, no disrespect or anything but I don't think you should say that about Chuck. Sir."

Sheriff Shit Head stood up so quick I thought he'd pass out from a drop in his blood pressure. No such luck. His face got real red. "What did you just say, boy?" he bellowed. "Did you just tell me what I can and can't do in my own jail? Is that what

96

you just did?"

Jerry turned whiter than usual. "No, sir," he squeaked. "Not at all, sir. I just thought, you know . . ."

"Boy, you don't think when yore a prizner in my jail, you unnerstand? I do the thinkin' here. Now, one more word outta either of you and you'll wish Jesus was here to save you." He paused. "Uh, you boys are Christians, right? Is either one of you a Jew?"

I wanted to remind him he told us not another word or we'd need Jesus to help us but decided to let it slide. He lifted his tomato can and let loose with another stream of brown spit.

"Well, are you?"

"Sir," I took a chance, "you said we had to shut up, remember?"

"Wal, you answer that. You boys Jews or Christians?"

I wanted to say we were Hindus, or followers of the Snake God. "Sir, Jerry and I are God-fearing Christians, right Jer?"

"Right, Mikey. We're Christians all right, Your Honor."

A slow sneer took shape on Sheriff Crucifixion's face. "Then lemme hear you boys recite John 3 and 16."

"Yes, Sir." Jerry began, *"The Lord is my shepherd . . . "*

"He's just kidding, Sir. It goes, *'For God so loved the world that he gave his only begotten son . . .'* " and before I could get to the part about not dying, the phone on Sheriff Asshole's desk rang. Before he answered it, another rivulet of spit splashed into the tomato can.

"This is the Sheriff . . . oh, hey, . What's up? He is? He did? Again? Okay, I'll be there in a minute. Got a couple of prizners here and we're having Bible class, but I'll come get him and put his drunk ass in the tank. Hold him 'til I get there. Naw, jest makin' these criminals quote me some scripture. On my way."

Before he walked out of the jail, he made very clear what would happen if we took off. "We've got a whole kennel full of hongry bloodhounds out back. They're sleepin' now, but if I wake 'em up they're ready to hunt down anybody that even thinks about leavin' without my permission. Really nasty dogs, boys, big ol' teeth, so y'all just stay right here 'till I git back. Ya hear?"

"Yessir," we both answered, as Sheriff Racist Pig closed the door behind him. We waited until we heard his car take off into the night to capture another law-breaking criminal.

Jerry said it first. "What the fuck? Are we in some Twilight Zone bullshit? This is really freaking me out, man. I mean, what if we wind up on a chain gang for the next 10 years?"

"Shut up! Don't even say that shit, man! Yeah, this could turn out pretty awful. Look, we've got to find Chuck. He's probably scared to death."

We walked over to the door marked "Jail," the one through which Chuck had disappeared, with Sheriff Ape Shit pushing him down the dark corridor. I opened it wide and shouted, "Chuck! Where are you? Are you in here?" He answered immediately.

"Yeah! Here! The end of the hallway."

We walked down to the cell where Chuck was being held. He was sitting on a metal cot bolted to the concrete floor.

Well," he said, "the I.D. card thing didn't work. He looked at it and said, 'Oh, you're a drug addict, too.' So, scratch that idea."

"Okay," I answered, "but we've got to get out of here. Fast. You know what can happen. Nobody knows we're here, I'm sure they think we're trying to register Negroes to vote, no shit we are in danger."

We froze. The door at the end of the hall opened. I could feel my guts tighten.

It was the cleaning woman, Maylene. "Who's here?" she half-hollered. "I hear y'all talkin'. Who's up in this jail?"

Chuck answered her. "Ma'm, it's just us, the ones the Sheriff brought in a few minutes ago. We're just trying to figure out what to do."

Maylene came slowly down the hall, still pushing her mop bucket. "Oh, it's y'all. Well, now, you boys are in trouble with this mean ol' Sheriff. I heard what he's been sayin' to you. He's not just talkin' to hear hisself talk. He already knows what he's gonna do with y'all. Iffn' you boys can get away, you better do it before he comes back. He's a terrible white man. He hates coloreds, and he hates it when he sees a white person even just talkin' to a colored person."

Yeah, well, we sure as hell didn't need to her that. Now it was absolutely certain we had to get out of here, away from this jail and this shitty little Southern hell-hole, Horse Fuck Crossing or whatever it was called, before Sheriff Death returned.

Chuck was looking closely at Maylene. He was staring at what appeared to be a bulge under her faded shirt. Then, I saw it, too. A faint outline of, what? a bag? her lunch?

"Ma'm," Chuck said quietly. "I think you might be able to help us."

Maylene quickly moved her hand to cover what Chuck had been staring at. "Now, you just never mind 'bout that. You boys are in trouble wit' the Sheriff and I've got to get these floors mopped." She started to push the bucket back towards the hall door.

"But," Chuck said, pointing to her waist, "I'm guessing I

know what that is. A bag of roots, maybe? And, other things, maybe things you use to help folks? You're a Root Lady?" Maylene stared at Chuck, her eyes growing brighter in the dim cell light. "Boy, how you know 'bout that? How you know what I am?"

"I know all about Root Ladies! My grandma told me about you all and I know from my neighborhood in New York. I know what Root Ladies can do."

Maylene stared at Chuck. "Now, why you talkin' like that in front of these white boys? They might tell on me. They might get me in trouble. Shame on you, now."

"Ma'm, they already know about Root Ladies. I told them all about it. No one's gonna tell on you." Jerry didn't know what the hell Chuck was talking about. He had slept through Chuck's tutorial. "But," he went on, "we need your help to get out of here. Please."

"Why you boys in here, anyway?" She turned to Jerry and me. "What y'all do? Couldn't be murder or the Sheriff woulda' put all y'all in a cell, too. Maybe worse than murder?" She paused, then slowly looked at each of us in turn. "Y'all here to sign folks up to vote? Is that it? You New Yawk boys down here to sign folks up?" she said to Chuck. "Lawd, that sho'nuff is worse than murder to these ol' Crackers. I don't know, now, and 'sides I ain't got the key to your cell, boy." She turned back to Jerry and me. "You two the ones got to figure this thing out."

I took a big chance. "Ma'm, we've already figured it out. It's like this: We need your help."

"He's right, Maylene," Chuck said. "Maybe you can put that Sheriff to sleep soon as he gets back and then we can get Jerry's car keys and be in Georgia before that fool wakes up. Please.

You know what might happen if we don't get out of here before that judge shows up. For real. Please, Ma'm."

Maylene continued to stare at Chuck, as though she was deciding if he was worth saving. Jerry and me? Since we were white I'm sure she didn't much care or figured we'd be okay regardless of what happened. After all, the Sheriff was white and white folks always stick together. Except for when they don't.

Finally, she spoke, quietly. "All right. I'll hep you, cuz If they kill you boys, we'll never get to vote. Won't no white folks come down here and show us how to do it. Now, Sheriff always wants a cup of coffee this time of the morning if he's here in the jail. I'll fix it for him and you boys will have your chance. And, I know where he keeps the keys to these here cells so you (she pointed at me) can get this colored boy on out of here and y'all can git."

The three of us tried to thank her at the same time. Jerry reached out to hug her, but Maylene gave him a look that said, no, I don't hug white folks. "He should be back soon, now, so I'll jest go in back and make his coffee." She pushed the mop bucket down the hall and disappeared around the corner.

Jerry was getting agitated. "Is this gonna work? What's a Room Lady? Will one of you tell me what's going on?"

"Root Lady, Jer," I answered. "Root. R-O-O-T."

"Okay, what's a R-O-O-T Lady? She gonna poison the Sheriff? Holy shit, man. Murder? We're gonna be charged with murder? In this jack-shit, backwoods hell-hole? Killing the fucking SHERIFF?! Are you serious??"

"Man," Chuck said, "keep your voice down. "There might be somebody here."

"Yeah, if there is we're gonna have to kill him, too. Right?

He's heard the whole plot! Jesus Christ, Mikey! A double murder? We're fucking doomed!"

"C'mon, man. Damn! No one's going to murder the Sheriff. Or anyone else. That cleaning lady, Maylene, knows how to heal people and help 'em sleep and all kinds of stuff. You slept through Chuck's story about Root Ladies. It's real. She'll put something in his coffee and he'll just nod off long enough for us to get the hell out of Horse Fuck and cross the state line. Then we're safe." Part of reassuring Jerry was to reassure myself. Ol' Sheriff Incompetent didn't take any prints or mug shots, so he had no way to identify us except by saying "two white boys and a nigger." Yeah, there's a description.

We walked back to our bench just as a car pulled into the gravel parking lot. A door opened and closed, and we could hear Sheriff Redneck warning someone. "Now, J.D., we're goin' into the jail and we're goin' real peaceful like and yore gonna sleep it off in one of the cells. No trouble, now, ya' hear? I don't wanna have to whomp yore ass with one of my dog chains. Is that clear? Peaceful. And quiet, too."

There was no answer, just a sullen grunt from J.D.

Jerry and I tried again to look interested in the wanted posters and announcements on the cork board. The door opened, and Sheriff Numb Nuts and a raggedy-assed looking redneck stumbled in, the redneck obviously drunk on his ass. "Now, I tole you. I don't want no trouble this time," the Sheriff again warned J.D. The guy was a wreck. Covered in mud and what appeared to be shards of shattered glass. His hair was matted, and god knows what kind of vermin were nesting there. He kept opening and closing his mouth like a fish in the bottom of a rowboat. I could see maybe two teeth still intact, although their yellow coating was a hint they soon would be broken off and spit out like the other 30 must have been.

"Whar you takin' me, Sheriff?" J.D. mumbled. "I don' wanna be 'round them dogs of yourn. Them bastards are vicious, should be put down, 'specially thet red devil, whut you call 'im? *Brute*? Las' time he damn near chewed off my arm, thet sumbitch."

"Well, J.D. that's cuz you ran." He looked at Jerry and me as he said that. "I done tole you, don't run. Brute knows to keep my prizners ri'cheer where I can watch 'em. So, this time, stay put 'les you want to give Brute another chance at yer arm." Sheriff Asswipe thought that last was funny, a real knee-slapper. He laughed the way I blow my nose.

Down the hall they went to the cell-block, such as it was. Three adjoining cells with nothing in each but a cement bunk. And Chuck. He was in the middle cell. In seconds, we could hear J.D. yell, "I ain't gonna be next to no nigger, Sheriff! You can put me out with them hounds, but I ain't gonna get thet close to no nigger!"

We could hear cell doors clanking open and shut as Chuck was moved to one of the end cells and JD. put in the other.

"Goddam," Jerry whispered. "These people are crazy, I mean totally, Mikey. That drunk redneck says he won't be in a cell – a goddam *jail cell*!? – if he's next to a colored guy? Man, we gotta get some distance between us and this bullshit."

"Patience, Jer. Maylene's *hoo-doo* is about to set us free."

After tucking JD into a cell with a promise that if he didn't behave the hounds chained out back would gleefully tear him to pieces, Sheriff Roscoe came back to the front office where Jerry and I were one again trying to act interested in the flyers and announcements taped to the walls and tacked to the bulletin board. Anything to avoid more bullshit from the county's top cop. We had heard enough from Roscoe. He sat down behind his desk and, after pushing a few papers around, leaned forward and bellowed at the closed hall door, "Maylene! Maylene! Git yore black ass in here! Where's my coffee?"

Footsteps shuffled down the hall, the door opened, and Maylene shuffled in, a stained mug of coffee in her hand.

"Yessuh, Sheriff, here I am. Yessuh, and here's that coffee, right here, just like you always like it – hot and black. Here it is." She put the mug on the desk in front of Sheriff Jerkoff. "That's a girl," he said, "and, you know whut?" he turned to Jerry and me with a shit-eating grin on his bloated face. "That's how I like my gals, too – hot and black!!! Haw-haw-haw . . ." His laughed was phlegmy and nasty sounding, like his throat was coming apart and sliding into his gullet. "Haw-haw-haw . . . now, thet's funny, right, Ohio? Like I like my gals!" And then another round of choking laughter. Jerry tried to laugh with him as a show of solidarity but could only manage a gagging sound.

We waited for Sheriff Jokester to take that first gulp of coffee, waiting to see how long it would take this buffoon to slump back in his chair, asleep. "Maylene always makes this way too hot," he said, indicating the mug with a nod of his head. "But she sure can make it good, too. Hot and black . . . haw-haw-haw. That's some funny shit, right, Ohio?"

Oh, yessir, Sheriff," I answered. "Funny, um, shit. Yes sir! Funny, right, Jerry?"

"Yeah, man, that's funny," Jerry added, his words dripping perfect Toledo sarcasm. "I mean really funny. 'Hot and black.' Wow! You just make that up, your Honor? Just right then? All by yourself, I mean? Like, boom! There it is?"

Sheriff Pissant gave Jerry a long, cold look. "Boy, yer not

mockin' me now, are you? Not getting' cutesy with me, right?"

"No, sir, I sure am not, no sir," Jerry answered, quickly glancing at me for some backup. I didn't have any. Not against this yahoo.

"Well, a damn good thing, boy. I don't like smart-ass Yankee boys come down here to cause race trouble. We take care of things in this town. Everybody knows their place and sticks to it and that's why our nigras don't get no fancy ideas. And, that's the way it should be. Nice and peaceful." He reached for the coffee, tipped the cup to his mouth and took a huge swallow.

"Gol' damn, that's good! Maylene," he hollered towards the jail door, "you damn sure know how to make a man a cup of coffee! Hey," he turned to us, "you boys wanna see an application to join the N-double-A-C-P? Funny as hell. Asts questions like, 'whut kinda car y'all live in' . . . and . . . 'how many of yore pickaninnies was born with a daddy.'" He started digging through some papers in his desk drawer. "Now, where'd that go . . . damn! . . ." He began to list to the left, slumping towards the side of the desk. "Maylene! . . . bring me my pills . . . I'm feelin' funny . . . girl! . . . where the hell . . ."

And that was it.

Thud.

His bulky ass slid off the swivel-chair and onto the floor. Out. Zonked. A goofy grin on his face revealed a bunch of rotting teeth. "Man," Jerry said, leaning over the desk to see if he was really out. "This cat needs to see a dentist! For real."

Maylene had been standing in the hallway behind the door the whole time, waiting to see when her pinch of root dust would lay the sucker out. She walked into the room, maybe strutted is a better way to put it, looked at the mound of white man slumped on the floor, and nodded her head in satisfaction.

"Sho' 'nuf works, thet ol' swamp weed. Yas indeed." A big grin worked its way across her ebony face. "Now, lemme git those keys and git yore fren' out thet cell back there and you boys better git. No tellin' how long this ol' white bastard gonna stay down. Works different ev'ry time someone swallers it." She reached into one of the desk drawers, came up with a key, and went down the corridor to free Chuck. Within a half-minute they both came back to the office. We could hear ol' JD shouting in the cell behind them, "Hey! How 'bout me? Get me outta hyar, too, y'all. Don' jest take the nigra! C'mon, y'all! Fair is fair, dammit! If this hyar is a jailbreak I got to go, too." When it dawned on him that no, we weren't taking him too, his tone changed. "Well, I'll tell you whut. Sheriff's gonna be mad as hell. I'd hate to be around when he ketches y'all. And he will, too. You'll see! He's got them dawgs and thet red un' will chew yore arm flat off!"

"There! I told you!" Chuck said. "These root ladies know stuff, they damn sure do." He turned to Maylene and gave her a hug. "Thank you, ma'm. Thank you. You may have saved our lives. Mine, anyway."

Jerry and I enthusiastically agreed. "Yes, ma'm. You have definitely set us free." Jerry decided to hug her, too, and again got that body language that said, uh, no better not, white boy. Then, surprise! she grabbed Jer and pulled him to her large bosom, just long enough for a deep blush to cover his face. Those were definitely the largest breasts he'd ever come in contact with and it must have made him a bit dizzy. Maylene was the first to release the hug and had to give ol' Jer a little push to get him to back away.

"Now, you boys go on. And stay on the main road cuz they'll be lookin' for you on them side roads. 'Bout thirty miles and you'll cross the state line. Nuthin' they can do once you cross thet line."

"But, what about you, Maylene?" Chuck whispered, pointing to the still unconscious Sheriff. "He's gonna be mad as ol' billy hell when he comes to."

"Don' worry 'bout me, darlin'. I been colored all my life and I know how to work some of these white folks, especially this fool. When ol' sheriff wakes up I'll be holdin' his head and sayin' *'wake up sheriff, oh, please wake up, let him wake up, Jesus'* and I'll be fussin' and makin' like this fool is the most important thing in the world and he'll believe me and for at least a week after he won't call me his nigger gal. He'll say my name. An' I'll tell him one of them slick Yankee boys musta' picked the locks and got out."

"Okay," I said, "but what about the other guy, J.D.? He must have heard everything."

"Him? J.D.? Shoot, that ol' man has trouble rememberin' his own name. And, anyway, everybody in the county knows he's crazy from drinkin' thet likker he makes out in the holler. Sheriff knows it , too. Won't believe a word he says. Now, you boys go on. You got to go. Good luck to y'all."

We opened the office door, ran into the parking lot, found the Olds exactly where we left it, jumped in, and sped away as though haints were about to catch us and drag us back to Horse Creek Crossing where ropes and hungry red hounds were waiting.

"Man, shit, damn, Jesus effin' Christ!" Jerry was yelling. "Floor this sumbitch and get me out of this fucking nightmare quick, Mikey. Go, go, go!"

Chuck was laughing. "Damn! I could hear that ol' cracker all the way in the back when he asked if you wanted to join the N-double-A-C-P. Then that slow fade as he slumped to the floor. Now, that's really some funny shit."

"You should have seen it, Chuck. His eyes started to roll up in his head and he had that shit-eating grin on his face and for a second, I thought maybe Maylene had decided fuck it and went ahead and killed him! 'Hot and black,' he said. Gotta wonder how many times Maylene has heard that?"

We drove on through the opaque Tennessee night, the sky on our left beginning to brighten as dawn approached, a sure sign we'd live to see another sunrise. We passed the state line several miles on and, according to Maylene, were now free. At last! *Thank god almighty!!*

Chapter 11

Mekkin

Mid-day was approaching, and we were getting hungry. At some point during the mad rush from Sheriff Roscoe's jail we had left the Dixie Highway and were now on US 19. And since we were in Georgia, Florida had to be close. "Getting' close to the beach, Jer, right Chuck?"

"Actually, there's still about 300 miles just to get to Florida. Then another couple of hundred to Tampa and on to Clearwater," he answered. So, there was plenty of time and considerable distance available to get trapped again in Southern hospitality.

We had decided not to stop for breakfast in north Georgia. No way to know if Sheriff Roscoe might have phoned a fellow lawman further south who would have been more than willing to snag a trio of trouble-making, race-mixing, law-breakers fleeing in a busted-up Oldsmobile with Ohio tags and no driver's licenses, two of them white agitators and the third one, as Sheriff Crazy would say, "a nigger drug dealer from New York who's probably armed." After feeling we had put sufficient miles between us and the Hounds of Horse Crossing we passed a sign for a barbecue restaurant that said, in huge red and yellow letters, "Just Ahead! The Pig 'n Chick Barbecue! Put Some South In Your Mouth! Y'all Come Stop Awhile. Good Eats."

I pulled into the crowded, gravel covered parking lot and found a space around back under a towering oak tree. In the rear-view mirror, I could see Chuck once again slump down out of sight to anyone walking nearby. And, again, I could feel the embarrassment of being white and knowing that it was the fear of whites that forced Chuck to do that. Wasn't he an American just like Jerry and me? Didn't he have the right to walk into a goddam barbecue joint and order a meal? Yes, to the first question, no to the second. That was the rule in the South.

"Here's a couple of bucks," Chuck said, handing me three dollars. "Just get me whatever that'll buy. Sandwich, platter, doesn't matter, pork or chicken. Barbecue is barbecue. And some sweet tea, okay? I'll stay out here so there's no trouble." Sweet tea? Chuck smiled. "That's what they call iced tea with sugar in it down here. Just say 'sweet tea.' They'll know what you mean. For god's sake don't ask for iced tea with sugar in it. That's one more clue you might be a Yankee agitator. It's 'sweet tea,' okay?"

So, once again, Chuck would stay in the car so there'd be no trouble. The realization that a black person couldn't do something as simple as go into a restaurant and have a meal had begun to really piss me off, ever since the freezing old guy in Lexington was told to go to the back door to get a hot cup of coffee. I couldn't understand how Chuck dealt with it in such a matter-of-fact way. But that's what it was: a matter of fact. And, after years of living with laws and rules – and, not just in the South – that had to be followed if a confrontation was to be avoided, Chuck simply acknowledged the reality those rules imposed – at least here in Georgia, or Tennessee, or Kentucky, wherever the Jim Crow rules applied. In the North, it was a different matter altogether. Some of the rules existed there as well, but the discrimination was subtler and therefore, in a very real way, more demeaning and insulting.

The restaurant was packed. A good thing we were ordering to go since there were no available tables or seats. It took a moment to realize nearly everybody was fat, really fat. Jerry had to comment, his voice lowered so only I could hear.

"What is this?" he whispered. "A fat-ass convention? Look at those women in the corner. They look like the Three Tons O' Fun!"

"The Tons O' Fun were males, Jer. Get your insults straight."

A waitress came over and placed two glasses of water and a large basket of napkins on the table. "Howdy, boys," she smiled. "Y'all are new here, right? Ain't seen y'all before. So, whut ya do is go git in that line ovah there and make your order. Then one of us'll bring it to yer table, unless you're ordering to go."

We were ordering to go. "Then stand over there and I'll bring it to y'all when it's ready." She pointed to a small table near the door. She was cute in a Sandra Dee kind of way, short, blond, bouncy. Jerry focused on the bouncy part.

"Well, it sure smells good in here," he said, giving Sandra Dee his best toothy smile. "Yeah, this is our first time in your restaurant, but, it sure won't be the last," he lied, his eyes starting at her eyes and moving slowly down to her black flats. "You sure are cute!" Oh, shit. Not again. He had to hit on whatever girl crossed his field of vision. The possibility of

111

more trouble loomed large. I just knew her boyfriend was six-three, had arms as big as my thighs, and probably worked at the local pulp-wood mill and on his way over right now to get some lunch and see his honey, the girl Jerry was grinning at.

"Are you from here?" Jerry asked, not knowing where the hell "here" actually was. But he was making his move. I just wanted to order, get our barbecue, and boogie on out.

"Naw, I'm from Mekkin, she answered.

"Mekkin? That's a funny name, right? Mekkin."

"You think it's funny?" Sandra Dee said, her hand on her hip and a look on her face that clearly said, you bein' a smart-ass, mister? "Well, then, where you boys from?" It sounded like a challenge. Jerry answered like he was telling a female member of a hunter-gatherer tribe that he was from a place that was civilized, with indoor plumbing and paved roads.

"Well, Honey, we're from up North. Toledo. O-Hi-Oh." He leaned back in his chair and gave Miss Dee the visual once over again. I was starting to see a bad ass-kicking in the parking lot when her huge boyfriend arrived.

"Uh, Jer, I'm sure she has work to do, right, Miss?" I looked up at her, trying to end this conversation as quickly as possible. But, ol' Jer just couldn't let it go.

"You ever been up North?" he asked, now with a smug look that seemed to say, *gal, I'm a travelin' man. Been all over. I know things. Stuff you'd never guess at in Mekkin.* Damn!

"So, you boys are Yankees, right? Yankees. Wal, I'll be." She turned to the woman behind the counter and said, in a voice loud enough to get most of the lunch crowd to stop talking and turn to look at these . . . Yankees, "How 'bout that, Clara Bee? Got us a couple a' Yankee boys here." Jerry looked pleased. He had the attention of the whole damn restaurant. Some of the people were smiling at our (my) embarrassment, some were frowning, and some were slowly shaking their heads as though we were a couple of piteously deformed high school students gone totally truant. Or a couple of Northern agitators come south to help Negroes register to vote.

"Wal," Sandra Dee said, satisfied her announcement had gotten so much attention, "so, whut you boys want to order?"

Jerry was about to say something lewd I was sure, so I ordered for both of us. And Chuck. "Um, we'll have two chicken platters, and a pork sandwich."

"You want tater tots with that?"

"Tater tots? What's that?"

"Really? It's potatoes; little ones, deep fried. Y'all don't have tater tots in Oh-Hi-Oh? My goodness."

"Yeah," I answered, "tater tots sound perfect."

While all this back-and-forth was entertaining to Jerry, I was ready to go. I wanted to get our order and get the hell away from so much Southern Fried bullshit. And, Chuck was waiting in the car. I didn't want any of these white folks to see him out there for fear they might accuse him of car theft. We got our orders and were paying the cashier when Jerry turned to Sandra Dee and said, "Seriously, where is Mekkin? How do you spell it?"

She looked at him, her head slightly tilted, an expression on her face that said, you must be the dumbest Yankee ever. In a voice loud enough for the crowd to hear she said, "How do I spell Mekkin? Really? It's M-A-C-O-N, Mekkin. Okay?"

As we hustled out the door, the crowd was still laughing.

We drove a mile down 19, turned onto a dirt road, and, after another hundred yards or so, found a shady pine near an old tree stump that made a perfect table. The food from the Pig n'

Chik was delicious. It was the first real southern barbecue Jerry and I had ever eaten. In Toledo, barbecue usually meant cook some meat on a grungy backyard grill, cover it in a vinegar-smelling sauce from the A&P, slap it on a plate, and there's your barbecue. Nasty stuff.

"One thing about the South, guys," Chuck offered, "it may be filled with racist assholes but the food is great, even though the recipes were stolen from black folk. That's what we do," he added, licking the remains of his pork platter off his fingers. "We cook food that lets us forget the day-to-day bullshit we have to deal with." I noticed Chuck's use of the pronoun 'we'. Up to that point he had referred to blacks as 'they.' Maybe he had made some sort of decision about Jerry and me, something close to trust. "I'm sure you boys have heard of 'soul food,' right?"

We hadn't. But, after Chuck described it to us, we realized how white people were missing out entirely on food that might not have been the healthiest, but was certainly comforting to the, well, soul.

We finished our barbecue and got back on the road.

We were in the North Georgia Mountains, part of the Appalachian range that stretches from Maine to Alabama. The small, mostly abandoned mountain towns we drove through and the sad, isolated shacks scattered through the rural landscape closed off whatever conversation we might have had about what we were seeing. The landscape seemed to demand muted conversation or silence, like what would be expected at a funeral. The sight of so much poverty was overwhelming. Nothing like this existed in Toledo. Yeah, we had poor people (hell, I was one) but poverty that existed in a city where nearly everyone worked a factory job was less obvious. Rural poverty, especially in these mountains, was not just visible and devastating, it was overwhelming. It went on for miles. Clusters of run-down shacks, some with broken windows taped over with tar-paper, the occasional crumbling chimney tilting insanely against the side of the building, the front porches sagging under the weight of discarded – or perhaps collected - appliances, broken sofas, metal milk cans, rusting bedsprings, car engines, stacks of sodden catalogues, coils of corroded wire some of it studded with still sharp barbs, 50-gallon barrels filled to the tops and spilling over with trash, twisting kudzu vines creeping up the leaning porch roof supports and crawling along the eaves; all evidence of overwhelming poverty and neglect. And, in the barren, packed-dirt front yards, always the little white kids, five or six at a time, looking as though they were hungry or malnourished, covered in dirt, with ragged shirts that dragged in the dust when they ran about the yard, screaming incoherently, chasing an emaciated dog, a chicken running for its life, or each other.

"Jesus Christ!" Jerry mumbled, staring out the window. "This is unreal. How do these people live? What's the point being alive in a place like this?"

Every mile or so we would pass an old man or old woman carrying a burlap sack or pulling a child's old, rusted wagon, walking slowly along the shoulder of the road, bending every few feet to pick something up and then dropping it into the wagon or stuffing it into the sack.

"They're collecting trash?" I asked absently. "Why would they collect trash? There's piles of it on their porches."

"That's not what they're doing," Chuck said. "They're foraging for food. They're pulling dandelion plants and wild onions and mushrooms, anything that's edible. It all goes into a cook pot with a chopped up squirrel or rabbit. It's what they do if they want to eat. I told you about my grandmother. Well, before she moved north she lived in Mississippi. When she was a kid, they had to do the same as what these white folks are doing. Trying to survive. Some things never change, man. A fucking pity isn't it. But this is America and if you can't make it on your own, no one gives a shit. Way it is, man. For real."

The sight of the crushing poverty contrasted, in a painful way, with the beauty of the countryside we were driving through. The Georgia mountains were solid and silent. They had been here forever and would remain here forever. The slopes were covered with the tallest pine trees we had ever seen, stretching up until they disappeared in the low-hanging clouds. Massive Oaks, Beech, Cedar, Weeping Willow, an endless forest that was both inviting and foreboding. We could only imagine the lives of the people who lived deep in these hills. We guessed they probably would not be too welcoming of a couple of white boys and a young black musician in a car with Ohio license plates.

The traffic was sparse, and the time slid away unnoticed. Every few miles we would pass another small gray or white cement block church, the marquee out front with a scary-ass message that was both a promise and a warning. *To Enter The Gates Of Heaven You Must Be Saved, Or You Will Burn In Hell Forever.* Ah, yes. That "burn forever" bullshit. Always the implied threat of eternal horror when you had a chance to believe in the little baby Jesus and refused to take it. Behind the church, the cemetery. Mud-colored, tilting gravestones, the inscriptions faded or worn to indecipherable scratches, out of place and out of time with the newer markers, one of which was next to a mound of freshly dug red clay, shoveled

116

out of a yawning trench being made ready for the remains of yet another heaven-bound soul.

"Can we go a little faster?" Jerry suddenly mumbled, turning away from the window through which he had been quietly staring, breaking the silence that had filled the Olds.

"S'matter, pal? Gettin' a little creeped out?" Truth was, I was the one getting nervous from that feeling of disorientation that can settle around you like a fluttering shroud when you are someplace that is so beyond your experiences, so alien to your senses, that there is the sudden yearning to be home, safe, where things make sense. But, you can't be there because you are a 17-year-old, running from your life, and now find yourself in the mountains of North Georgia. All you can do is keep going. Keep going.

Finally, a sign that said "Atlanta – 120 Miles." Civilization! The big city! Life, laughter, movies, restaurants, away from this poverty-racked landscape where open graves about to be filled just really fucked up your entire day.

"So. Chuck. What do you know about Atlanta?" I asked.

He, too, had been staring out the window. He stretched his legs, lit one of his Kools, took a deep inhale, and let the smoke drift slowly around his head. "Not a whole lot. I do know it's where the Civil War was really lost, when Sherman burned it to the ground. Believe it or not, I had some family way back that lived in Atlanta. I guess they were slaves. Don't know too much about those old times. I know a lot of black folks are living there now. I've heard that Atlanta's trying to avoid the race stuff that's all over the South, sit-ins and demonstrations and trying to register to vote. Supposed to be a lot easier in Atlanta. I think all the real ugly shit's going on in Alabama and Mississippi. I saw that movie 'Gone With

The Wind' in New York. Weird shit, man, ol' Mammy runnin' around steppin' and fetchin' for the white folks. And, that gal Prissy, the one who said, 'I don' no nuffin' 'bout birffin' no babies, Miss Scarlett.'" Chuck laughed when he said it. "Some of my friends and I had just finished a gig at the Apollo and decided to go see the midnight showing at one of the theatres in Midtown. Laughed our asses off, man, for real. Especially when they burned that city to the ground. Damn! We cheered and got some shitty looks, believe me."

"What's the Apollo?" Jerry asked. "What's Midtown?"

Chuck smiled. "Black folks' theatre in Harlem, which is in New York. So's Midtown. In New York. You know about Harlem?"

"Of course," Jerry said, trying to let Chuck know he wasn't completely naive even if we were from Toledo. "It's where all the colored people in New York live, right?"

"Right, Jerry," Chuck answered, "all the colored people in New York live there. You got it, pal." The sarcasm flew by Jerry without a ripple in the smoke from Chuck's cigarette.

Atlanta, our map showed, was a little more than half-way between Toledo and Tampa. I had been driving the entire way and had stopped swallowing Christmas Trees the night before. Too much amphetamine and you get a king-hell headache, which is exactly what I now had. A real temple-pounder and the nausea that comes with it.

I took a chance and asked Jerry to drive while I got some sleep in the back seat. The last thing I said before closing my eyes was, "Don't fucking get us in a wreck, okay? I don't want to die on a road in Georgia." I drifted off to Jerry's maniacal giggle, the same laugh that woke me up a few hours later, his half-chuckle that segued into, "What the fuck . . .?" I pulled myself up and immediately fell back onto the seat, smacked down by a wave of nausea. Try again. This time I made it to a barely upright position, dizzy, feeling like a scoop of sand had been poured under my eyelids, my stomach churning. It was getting dark. The sun was setting, and the sticky fragrance of magnolia blossoms flooded the car. That had to be the source of my nausea. "What?" I said to both of them. "What do you mean, 'what the fuck?' What's going on?"

Chuck was slouched down in the front seat, again, an unlit Kool clenched in his teeth. Jerry was driving very slowly, half-turned to his left, staring out his side window. He said it again. "What the fuck?"

"Just keep driving, okay?" Chuck said. He twisted around in the front seat staring at the same thing Jerry was. It was obvious Chuck was scared. I forced myself to sit completely up and looked out the rear window, off to the side of the road where a huge billboard had been erected. The words were obviously hand-painted, large, threatening. The sign was double-sided, built in a V-shape, the point of the V aimed at the road, so it could be read from both directions simultaneously. At the top, the Confederate battle flag, the Stars and Bars, a symbol as well defined as the Nazi swastika. But it was the warning on the sign in six-foot-high, deep black lettering that was so ominous:

WARNING TO ALL NEGROES: DO NOT LET THE SUN SET WITH YOU STILL IN FORSYTH COUNTY.

I was stunned. I had never seen anything like this, a display of hate so public, so visible, especially to anyone traveling US 19. The threat was explicit, but it was left to the imagination as to what might happen to a colored person who was still in the county when the sun *did* set. A beating? Tossed into the county jail? Lynching? And then, another sign on the right side of the highway, this one smaller, welcoming travelers to Cumming, Georgia, the Forsyth County seat. *"The friendliest small town east of the Mississippi."* The juxtaposition of the two signs was insane. Which was true? If we had known the history of Cumming there would have been no doubt which to believe: for whites, the welcome sign; for blacks, the warning.

As was true in so many small southern towns during the Jim Crow era, it didn't require much to incite the white residents to a fury of racial violence. In Cumming, Georgia, on an early fall Sunday evening three years before the release of the film "Birth of a Nation," a local white woman was raped and murdered, her body discovered by teenagers walking to Sunday night services at the town's Baptist Church. Rumors insisted she was raped *after* she was killed. The crime scene was a scene of horror, with the woman's legs nearly severed from her torso. A black man who lived in the county was immediately charged and indicted for the crime. Two days later the man was shot, dragged from the Cumming jail and, still alive and screaming his innocence, hanged from a telephone pole in the center of town. The next day a coroner's inquest found the cause of death to be the gunshot. Regardless, the locals knew the man had been given appropriate Southern "justice" for black men accused of touching, winking at, or staring at a white woman: lynching. The penalty for *raping* a white woman was dismemberment.

"Let's just get out of here," I said. "That sign is an absolute mind-fuck"

"Which sign?" Jerry cackled. "The one that says this is the friendliest place ever? Or that big one that says once the sun sets ol' Chuck here can't stop and get a colored ice cream cone?

Yee-Haw!!"

"Real funny, asshole," I said, hoping our hitch-hiking companion had been around Jerry long enough – and it didn't take long at all – to get Jerry's sense of humor. Chuck sat upright, turned to Jerry, and smiled. At least, in the gathering darkness, I thought it was a smile. Maybe not.

Atlanta was just 30 miles down the road, and within an hour US 19 had become Roswell Road which had, in turn, become Peachtree Street. We were in the beating heart of the South.

The city's size was impressive, especially after the small towns and mountain villages we had driven through. For Jerry, however, Atlanta was a disappointment.

"Well, this sure as hell is not what I expected, Mikey," he said. "It looks like Toledo without the black snow. Where's the magnolia trees and mint juleps and Southern Belles?"

Chuck laughed. "It's all here, man. You have to get off the main drag a bit. I have an aunt who lives in Marietta, just a few miles from here. She has a big ol' magnolia tree in her front yard. As far as mint juleps and Southern Belles, well, that's not my Aunt Clara's style. She doesn't drink."

"Damn, Chuck," Jerry said, looking in the rear-view mirror. "You've got relatives all over the South!"

"Yeah, I do. My Aunt Clara moved here so she could go to Spelman College. White colleges in the South wouldn't admit her. Got her degree in science and went on to become a nurse. Of course, she could only treat colored patients in a colored doctor's office or in the Negro wing of a hospital. But, see, that was typical of what happened to Negro families. The ones that could, moved to the cities. They didn't want anything to do with working on some white man's farm. Had enough of that shit, trust me. Black folk were safer in the cities than isolated in the country or some ratty little red-neck town. The Night Riders, the Klan, couldn't come galloping through a city burnin' folks' homes down. In the country? Happened all the time. So, yeah, I have an aunt who lives near here."

As fascinating as Atlanta might be, it was not our destination. Clearwater was, with a stop in Tampa. So, on we went. Highway 19 had become Highway 41. It was all the same to us. Highway whatever. We just wanted to get to the beach.

I was feeling just a bit melancholy knowing that when we split company with Chuck I would lose what had the potential to become a genuine friendship. In listening to him, in the short time we had spent together since Jerry and I picked him up in Lexington, I had learned what seemed like secrets most whites would never know. Our time together had been compressed, and because of the red-neck bullshit we had been exposed to, bullshit that was either hysterically funny or potentially lethal, my high school buddy and I were seeing first-hand a small slice of what black folk had to deal with daily. Travelling with him through the deep South and watching how cautious he had to be – always aware that he could be threatened in a way Jerry and I could not – gave us two white boys a brief insight into what a young black man in the South, even if he was only passing through, had to endure. We hadn't yet reached the point where we understood it was close to the same reality Chuck had to deal with in the North as well.

We passed through a few more small towns south of Atlanta, each one preceded by, and then giving way to, fields of exploded cotton bolls, acres of peanuts, miles of soybeans. I assumed Jerry was asleep again in the back seat, but suddenly he shattered the silence with a shriek.

"Well, fuck me runnin'! We're coming to Mekkin! Where

that girl's from, that waitress, right? Mekkin, Jawja. I'll be damned!" He was pointing to a sign that read "Macon 15 miles."

"Man, damn!" Chuck said. "You just scared the hell outta me!"

"Me, too, asshole," I added. "Don't do that, okay?"

"Yeah," Jerry said, "but, it's real. Mekkin. I get it! I wonder how she'd pronounce Marietta?"

"May-retta," Chuck said. "Different way of sayin' shit down here. Makes 'em all sound ignorant and half-educated. Like, how would you pronounce 'Ponce de Leon'?"

"The Fountain of Youth guy? The explorer?"

"Yeah."

"Pon-suh day Lee-own."

Chuck laughed. "Right. But, there's a street back in Atlanta, long one, with that name and people there pronounce it 'Ponce duh LEE-on.'" He laughed again. "Rednecks are so damn funny when they're not tryin' to lynch you."

A few miles south of Macon Jerry took over the driving. We had changed seats just before we entered a completed section of the new Interstate Highway system, I-75, and it took me less than a minute to drift into a deep sleep.

Jerry was shaking me. "Wake up, Mikey! Wake up! We're in Florida! We made it! We're here!" My eyes wouldn't open. My eyelids felt like they were stuck together with library paste, a substance that will forever smell like elementary school.

"We just passed the sign," Jerry said, twisting around to get one more look. "It said 'Welcome to Florida. The Sunshine State.' There were palm trees around it! Wow! Palm trees!" Jerry was easily impressed. Part of his charm.

The next sign we passed said: Tampa 200 miles. "We're not

there yet, man," Chuck added. "By the way, the oil light's on. We better pull over. Don't want to blow your engine."

We pulled into the first rest stop we came to. It was entirely different from the roadside "parks" we had passed coming through Kentucky and Georgia. This had indoor toilets, and maps, and picnic benches, and a maintenance man mowing the close-cropped grass. Obviously, Florida wanted to make an impression since every traveler meant money in the state treasury.

The sky was Florida blue. Puffy sub-tropical clouds drifted by. The air smelled of . . . flowers? Bushes? Florida itself? Did Florida have its own distinctive smell? Toledo sure as hell did. In Toledo, it was burning rubber and hot metal and oil refineries and car exhaust. Here it was different. Once you've smelled Florida, you never forget the fragrance.

Tampa: 150 miles. We had dumped three more quarts of oil into the engine, our last of the 24 quarts we had started with, and got back on this new highway, Interstate 75. There were very few cars on the road, and I thought what a waste of money building these super highways. Where would all the traffic come from? We noticed the highway numbering signs were now in color; reds and yellows and blues, totally different from the dirty grey and black signs in Ohio and all the states we had passed through.

Tampa: 75 miles. "You gonna miss us, Chuck?" Jerry asked. He leaned over the front seat and bummed yet another Kool from Chuck's seeming endless supply. ("Part of being a blues player, man. Smokin' cigs, drinkin' whiskey. It's all good.")

"Sure, I'll miss you two. It's been an interesting, what? two days? three? Seems like longer than that, doesn't it? Time just rips by when you're having fun, and god knows this has been fun." I couldn't tell if Chuck was being sarcastic again or sincere. It didn't matter. He was a good guy either way.

Tampa: 50 miles. We were passing orange groves and cattle ranches, with weird looking cows that we found out later were American breeds that had been crossed with cattle from India, the better to tolerate the Florida heat. The huge extended horns on their heads and weird, droopy flaps of cowhide that hung from their necks gave us a sense of being experienced travelers. I mean, who among our friends back in Toledo had ever seen animals like these?

Then: Welcome to Tampa! The sign had an exclamation point after the word Tampa, as though this was the destination you've been heading for your entire life. In our case, that was almost true. Toledo seemed like a bad dream, a place where you could see the air, smell the water, breathe a mix of drifting industrial shit that contained, what? Who knew? It was a secret. A secret we wouldn't find out about until much later when people started dying of lung and liver disease. But, for now? Toledo was part of the industrial might of the free world, a piston in the engine of progress, a blessing the rest of the world could only hope to copy. To Jerry and me, it was a place to see getting smaller and smaller in the rear-view mirror.

But, not Tampa. Tampa was clean and bright and silvery blue. We couldn't imagine how Clearwater could top this. Unless it was Paradise. We drove through downtown until we came to Lafayette Street. On Chuck's directions we turned right and crossed the Hillsborough River. On our right, the domed spires of Tampa University. On our left, *The House of Seven Sorrows* coffee shop. We pulled down a side street and parked. He leaned up from the back seat to face both Jerry and me. "Well, here we are, fellas. My destination. Where I'll be playing for the next two weeks."

"Then, where," I asked?

"Dunno. Maybe Miami, maybe I'll head for the Keys. I've heard Key West is where you go when there's no place left to go. Sounds to me like a challenge."

"You're pretty cool," Jerry suddenly said. I thought he was going to add "for a colored guy" but, he didn't.

"You, too, man."

"Well, Chuck," I said, "this has been pretty crazy. We're glad we met you, right, Jer?"

"For sure."

"So, good luck, okay?"

"Same to the two of you," Chuck said as he opened the door, pulled out his duffel and his guitar, and stepped into the street. "If you get the chance come on over from your Aunt's one night and I'll put you on the guest list."

"Hey, that's great," Jerry said. "That means we get in free, right?"

We watched as Chuck walked to the front door of the coffee house. He paused for a moment, leaned his guitar against the building, and waved.

As things turned out, we never did go to the *House of Seven Sorrows* to hear Chuck play.

Book Two

Chapter 12

Rock And Roll

I moved to Atlanta in October, 1974. The city was in transition, changing from a medium-size Southern city into what it was to become over the next four decades: A massive megalopolis with a population approaching six million with millions more expected. But, in 1974 it was still possible to find in Atlanta the fulfillment of whatever ambition had been growing in one's imagination. City planner? The opportunities were endless. Politics? If you had the guts for a fight against the right-wing crazies who were fully involved in total resistance to Atlanta's developing image as the art center of the New South, this was your city. Theater? Drama companies were sprouting around the city like mushrooms after a rainstorm. Dance? New York South. Writing? The roster of Atlanta-based, critically acclaimed novelists was expanding exponentially. Southern rock 'n roll? The city bled rock 'n roll. Ditto jazz, blues, and music that defied description. And, if you fell in love, even just for a moment, the magic of warm, magnolia-perfumed Southern nights would magnify the erotic; the smooth texture of skin against skin, breath dissolving into breath, sex that pushed to the limit of sensuality, a soul connection that would last forever, certainly until the next sensual, erotic, endless, *etc., etc.,* came along, as it certainly would, more often than not before the week was out.

The time, therefore, was perfect for the romance of a rock and blues festival. A big one; city-size and one Atlanta would remember. I decided to do it.

The first order of business was to construct a production company. I had met several interesting people shortly after I arrived: Jack, who was on his way to becoming a film and stage actor; Tom, his brother, who knew how to baffle people with bullshit and in the process separate them from wads of cash; Mike, who would eventually earn his PhD. in biochemistry but for the time being was an excellent reefer and coke connection; Katy, an artist who worked in soft sculptures as well as being a budding photo-journalist; Don, who had money but was generally a total fuck-up; and, finally, Cat and Ira, owners of a talent agency that represented a growing stable of talented, but as yet unknown, Southern Rock musicians. And, that was it. The company. We decided to call ourselves, "The Atlanta Rock Conspiracy." And, since everything must have a name, I christened the yet-to-be concert, "Revival." The name had such a Southern vibe. *Traveling tent meetings. Salvation. Wednesday night prayer meetings. Baptisms by the river. Snake handling for those trusting in the Lord! Glory! REVIVAL!*

Next, we needed a date and a venue. I decided on April 20, about four months away from our first organizational meeting. I chose that date because my search through an encyclopedia found nothing in recent history that occurred on April 20 i. I didn't want to overlap with a holiday of some sort. It was only later, after contracts had been signed and the date agreed to by all the parties involved, that I discovered April 20 did, in fact, have a certain significance: It was Adolph Hitler's birthday. Fuck.

For the venue we focused on a crumbling granite, outdoor, bowl-shaped structure, Chastain Amphitheater, in Buckhead, one of the city's upscale neighborhoods. It had opened in 1944, but with WWII still tearing the world to pieces there was no promotion of events. Eight years later, the city of Atlanta took ownership and began offering free concerts by the Atlanta Pops Orchestra. And, then, it died a second time. Once again, it sat empty, forlorn, waiting for the right circumstance to bring it to life for a third time. That would be us, the Atlanta Rock Conspiracy. The city's Parks and Recreation Department was eager to get something, anything, of a musical nature into Chastain. Sort of a "prime the pump" event. If the ARC could produce a successful concert, other production companies surely would be interested. The city charged us one dollar rent and the deal was made.

Then came the talent. We started at the top. We offered slots to the Allman Brothers Band. (*"You boys must be crazy! The Brothers don't do amateurish bullshit."*) Marshall Tucker Band. (*"We'll pass."*) Richie Havens. (*"He's having dental surgery that week."*) Ah, but our ace in the hole was the agency owned by Cat and Ira! They had the talent! Just not the Allman Brothers or Marshall Tucker or Richie Havens. They had local talent, which meant excellent bands that were waiting to be discovered and signed to a contract by the right record label A&R (Artists and Repertoire) person.

Word of our concert production company had gotten out and was the subject of much speculation: Who are these people, this ARC? Where did they come from? What's their experience?

Of course, that added to the cryptic nature of our little band of Conspirators. We held no press briefings, gave no interviews to the various radio stations, released no updates as to the talent signed, had no known business address (other than my Midtown apartment), no published phone number, no anything. I mean, what the fuck? We were the Atlanta Rock *Conspiracy!*

After we secured the venue, we got busy putting together everything necessary to the inner workings of a rock concert: tickets, security, emergency medical techs, concessions, stage hands including the set-up/take-down crew needed to move the bands on and off the stage as quickly as possible, lighting and a lighting technician, sound equipment and a sound engineer, mics, on and on, a seeming endless list of components needed to pull this rock and roll concert together.

And money.

We needed a steady cash flow and something in reserve. Our start-up money, five hundred dollars, came from Don the Fuck-Up. Through the clandestine network we were slowly building we managed to secure a few thousand more from a couple of rich, white, Atlanta boys who were determined to piss off their Conservative, church-going parents by giving money to these undesirables who were going to produce a debauched rock concert. *Outside, for God's sake! With drugs! And naked people running around under the influence of LSD and all sorts of other demon-inspired filth!* And, the boys promised more cash as needed, which turned out to be bullshit because the boys were sent back to military school, Spring vacation cancelled, as soon as Mummy and Father learned what they were planning. The boys had to be made unavailable to Mummy and Father's business and social acquaintances, post haste. *Can you imagine the scandal? It would be worse than getting one of the neighbor girls preggers. Mummy could always secure a Mexican abortion and Father could pick up the tab, plus give the kids a week on the beach at Cozumel when the ugliness had been all taken care of and made to go away. I mean, think of the boy's future! With a baby? A curtain-climber? No Yale like Father? No Whiffenpoofs? No tables down at Mory's? To the place where Louie dwells? In a pig's ass!!* But of course the problem was not knocking up one of the neighbor girls. The problem was rock n' roll.

At some point we outgrew my apartment and needed an honest-to-god office space, one that was rent free. We knew something would materialize. It usually did. Each time we seemed to hit the proverbial wall, someone would show up and help us solve whatever unsolvable problem was staring us in the face. And, here they were! Three guys who, together, owned a small music club – The Bistro - in one of the many run-down, drug-infested, hippie-blasted neighborhoods near the city's center: Hugh, Michael, and Jimmy. They gave us two rooms on the second floor of their building, an old house marked for eventual tear-down. Hugh was the business guy, Jimmy the musician, and Michael the hairdresser. Each of them thought the idea of a Rock Conspiracy was so fucking cool it dripped icicles. Jimmy was formerly part of a well-known Southern gospel music family. He was the proverbial prodigal son, the son of one of the crazed evangelicals, the one who sang bass and passed around the collection plate. Jimmy had gone completely off the rails and abandoned the whole Jesus scam and all that went with it, including the arm-waving, eye-rolling, repetitious, cacophonous bullshit that passed for "gospel music." Drugs and rock n' roll became his new twin Messiahs. The club-owning trio's senior partner, he had slow eyes and a sluggish way of talking which meant you had to be patient and wait quietly when he was saying something, anything, even the fucking weather prediction for that particular day. He was an absolute hoot. Hugh, with his beatific smile was more ethereal and New Age-y, which was fine with the ARC so long as he continued to help feed money to the constantly hungry little creature the ARC was becoming, bless its heart. Michael? He spent his days cutting and coloring the tresses of Atlanta's hip yuppie crowd and his nights at the club getting wasted with yet another tall, slim, smiling beauty who went all glassy-eyed and wobbly by ten o'clock.

We had determined at the beginning not to devolve into a mercenary, greedy, loud-mouth, dream-destroying concert production company. There were enough of those about and we wanted the world – okay, the world of Atlanta – to know we were truly a rock music counter-culture entity. The concert business had changed dramatically since Woodstock. No longer peace, love and music, the business of it all had morphed into a ravenous hydra that seemed to want human sacrifice along with the rock n' roll. So many extremely talented musicians disappeared into the maw of the big, nationwide production/recording companies never to be heard from again. We were to be the dragon slayers! The little production company that would return the music to the people! *Power to the people! Hooray for the people! People rule! People power! Down with the tyranny of Corporate Rock and Roll!* And, like that.

The most visible evidence of that commitment was found in our ticket price. While the Monster Companies were charging as much as fifteen dollars per ticket to see The Who and an opening act, we set our price at two dollars in advance, three at the gate. And that was for an all-day concert! Ten hours of glorious Rock, Folk, and Blues, along with a light show designed to separate the audience from the shreds of reality they might still be able to manage after eight hours of hard core "music from the people," the merciless Southern sun and whatever drugs they had swallowed. When night fell, the colors of the mind would be set free. I mean, rock and roll forever, right?

As we got closer to the concert date, we realized we needed to hook up with some sort of Atlanta non-profit to further imprint the righteousness of our mission. We decided on two counter-culture media outlets: the relatively new alternative radio station, WRFG (Radio Free Georgia), and the decade old Voice Of The Radical South, the ultra-Left weekly tabloid, The Great Speckled Bird, named, not ironically, after an old Southern hymn the words of which were based on the Biblical Book of Jeremiah, chapter 12, verse 9: *"Mine heritage is unto me as a speckled bird; the birds round about are against her; come ye, assemble all the beasts of the field, come to devour."* Once we connected the ARC to these two voices of Atlanta's radical underground our identity was secure, and we were convinced our name would live forever.

April 20 was approaching faster than we anticipated. By now we had our bands booked and they certainly were an eclectic collection of musicians: The Reverend Pearlie Brown – gritty blues and trenchant gospel from a very old singer who had been there at the Creation; The Last Great Jive-Ass Jug Band – hootchie-cootchie music reminiscent of frontier whorehouse bands; Marshgrass – electric mountain blues infused with calming rhythms from the Celtic Highlands ; Rock Mountain – Airplane and Dead-inspired jam band; EQT – the South's premier lets-get-drunk-and-fuck bar band; Flood – lost in Pink Floyd, never to return to Earth; Carrie Nation – think Allman Brothers without Dickie Betts; Darryl Rhoades and The Ha-Ha-Vishnu Orchestra – try to imagine a snowy summer day with bats flying around carrying tiny hand grenades they occasionally dropped and you might get close to understanding the Ha-Ha-Vishnu Orchestra; Warm – awwwwww . . . . make-out music with entwined, naked bodies while the parents are off playing Double Canasta; Rita Godfrey – sultry jazz and blues vocalist whose singing made every Lesbian in Atlanta want to have her child.

Yes, indeed. Eclectic.

The required psychedelic light show would be produced by the Kaleidoscopic Light Co., whose owner, The Wizard, was known as a magician who did beautiful and seeming impossible things with massive screens, projectors and beams of multi-colored light. And, if a given audience wasn't all that thrilled with his display of light-magic or wasn't paying that much attention, he would launch a barrage of pyrotechnics that would definitely get them to focus. He was a goddam genius.

For security, we enlisted one of the cults that had formed around the endless number of Tibetan or East Asian hucksters who had set up shop in the US after realizing that Yuppie Americans had a hunger for a belief system that was less bloody and restrictive than Christianity. The spiritually starved devotees were willing to spend whatever it took to get close to a Westernized faux *Nirvana*, skipping past the scary stuff that came with LSD or psilocybin or the Hare Krishna spinning dervishes. The sect we settled on was the Indian Guru Maharaj Ji's Divine Light Mission, because this gang was willing to work free and had a way of calming a drunk or stoned concertgoer by simply surrounding him or her and staring at them. And chanting stuff. Go figure.

Our first aid contingent was under the control of a local nurse who wanted some experience in crisis medicine. What better place to get that experience than a rock festival where there was always the possibility of massive head injuries when stoned rock-and-rollers might try to launch off the nearest promontory because they suddenly knew they could fly!

And then we hit the wall. At one of the final meetings with the City of Atlanta bureaucrats, the head of the Parks Department called us to his office and said he saw on one of the posters we had distributed that the concert was to run from noon until 10 o'clock that evening.

"That's just impossible," he said. "Can't happen. We have strict rules about Chastain. Four-hour music events only. Four hours, no more." And, he said it with glee. He had been one of the dead-enders who had opposed our gig from the beginning. "A noisy concert like that will result in drugs and sex and violence, all out in the open and causing the neighbors great embarrassment, not to mention lawsuits," he said, as though the words were on a cassette tape running endlessly in his head. He had been overruled by the Mayor, although it was the Mayor's staff, all young people, who convinced His Honor that a

massive rock concert in the middle of one of the city's upscale neighborhoods was, for sure, an excellent idea.

But we hadn't anticipated this. No one had. This rule had not been mentioned in the original meetings with the city administrators. And now, this official was almost twitching with delight when he informed us all our work was for nothing.

Bullshit. We were the Atlanta Rock Conspiracy and we would not be defeated. Never! *Excelsior!*

I tried threats. "If the concert doesn't go on for the ten hours we advertised we might have thousands of people in the streets rioting. I know the city doesn't want that, right?"

"Not my problem, boys," he replied. "My job is to enforce the rules. And, the rules say four hours. Take it or leave it. And, I hope you're not threatening me with violence! I would be very upset if you are. Very upset."

Take it or leave it? Obviously, he didn't know who he was fucking with.

After the meeting with this bureaucratic spoiler, we had a second meeting with the Mayor's young staffers. Rob, one of the people in the Bureau of Cultural Affairs, had the solution.

"Simple, really. The rules also say if the City co-sponsors an event at Chastain, the time restriction doesn't apply. You can go the full ten hours. We'll get the Mayor to sign off on this and you guys are all set." So, now, not only were we legitimate, we were by God official! The concert was to be a *co-production* of the City of Atlanta and The Atlanta Rock Conspiracy!!

See what I mean? Brick wall? Solution. Never failed. We were amazed. Slow-talking Jimmy said it was because, "We. . . are . . . a . . .righteous . . . group. We . . . are . . . filled . . . with . . . love . . . and . . . the . . . spirit . . . of. . . brotherhood . . . in . . . a . . . world . . . torn . . .asunder . . . by . . . greed . . . and . . . other . . . vicious . . . shit. . . like. . . war."

True, that.

Then, as though we were snake bit and all going to die, we got more upsetting news. We were broke. Tapped out.

Victory? Meet Defeat.

"We're down to $75 and change," Ira informed us. "And,

we still have bands to pay, not to mention printing costs, insurance, radio ads, and money for the four off-duty cops who insist on being here just in case there's a riot. And they charge time-and-a-half what the city pays them."

Damn. Stuck. And the concert date was two weeks away.

Hugh said he had a crazy idea. He called a meeting. "Look, I know a guy who is part of the so-called 'Gainesville Dealers Association,' you know, that group in Florida who dropped a bag of money in front of Jackson Memorial Hospital in Miami so that little kid could get his brain tumor operation? The one whose parents were pleading for help to save their kid's life? Thousands of dollars, all cash, and a pointed note in the bag with the money that condemned a system that would let a child die because his parents were too poor to afford an operation. Remember that?"

We did. It was a super act of compassion by a bunch of pot dealers who wanted everyone to know there was righteousness to be had in selling weed. They also had made several other contributions to causes that seemed hopeless for lack of money.

"Yeah, but, c'mon, man, this is a rock concert," Jack said, stating the obvious. "Not a kid's life-and-death operation. Big difference, pal."

"I'm not suggesting charity, guys. I think they'll lend us the money. We'd have to pay it back out of gate receipts. But, that'll give us the cash flow we need right now. What do y'all say?"

We all said, hell yes. Give it a try, Hugh. What's to lose? He went down the club's dark, musty hallway to Jimmy's office and made the call.

The GDA said yes, they would give us the money we needed

to complete the concert. Give it to us, not lend it. No pay-back required. It was that simple. They said their decision was based in part on the fact we were charging only two dollars per ticket; that the music did belong to the people who wrote and performed it and, ultimately, the people who listened, not asshole promoters and greed-head record companies. A little over the top with the anti-establishment attitude, but, so what? They had cash. We needed cash. They asked one thing in return: At some point during the concert we were to make an announcement from the stage on their behalf, not to praise their charitable work, but to further suggest there was something severely fucked up about a nation that would spend billions of dollars on weapons of death and destruction, and let millions of its own citizens, especially children, go without proper nutrition, housing, decent public schools, and medical care. There was no question they and we were singing from the same hymnal.

That was a Sunday. On Tuesday we were to meet their representative at Jimmy's house in the suburbs. Tuesday turned out to be a warm April day, the sort of day that makes visitors to Atlanta want to stay forever: Blue skies and the perfume of thousands of blooming dogwoods, azaleas, and countless numbers of flowering plants that turned Spring in Atlanta into a sensual cascade of color and exotic fragrances.

We Conspirators were sitting on the back deck drinking coffee and having a morning joint when a shiny, stunningly black Mercedes sedan turned off the street into the driveway and drove slowly toward the back of the house where we were waiting. "They're here," Hugh half-whispered, unable to take his eyes off the Benz. The car was so beautiful, for a moment I thought Hugh was going to tear up. "Oh, my God," he said, a slight tremor to his voice. "It's a Staff Car. It's a goddam 1940 Staff Car." Hugh, we discovered, worshipped the Mercedes brand. He went pale, like he was about to faint. "It's a Nazi High Command Staff Car. Hitler rode around in one of these! *Hitler!*"

Yes, and we had a concert scheduled for his birthday. Hitler's, not Hugh's.

The car stopped and for a moment no one moved; not us, not the people in the Mercedes. No one spoke. Near total silence. The birds continued to sing their territorial songs in the trees surrounding Jimmy's substantial back-yard; fat carpenter bees buzzed around the deck, looking for a place to start drilling; a Piper Cub stuttered across the sky. A neighborhood dog was barking. I'm sure there was childhood laughter somewhere in the distance. It was a moment.

Finally, reverently, Hugh and Jimmy stepped off the deck and walked over to the car. The driver stepped out and nodded to both. He was wearing black jeans, and a pale blue Miami Dolphins tee-shirt. It was easy to see he had muscles in places where most people don't even have places. His sunglasses were designer and very, very dark. He handed Hugh a brown paper bag, the top folded over several times and a thick rubber band keeping it all in place. The driver gave Hugh and Jimmy a friendly smile and waved to the rest of us sitting on the deck. We waved back, looking, I'm sure, like a circle of psychiatric patients out for an airing on visitors' day.

Finally, the car's doors opened, and the two passengers got out. I immediately thought the names Gunsel and Destroyer would fit these guys perfectly. Everyone then came up on the deck and, after a moment of scraping chairs, and shifting bodies, we all found seats around the metal patio table.

"Well, hello, everybody," the driver said. "My name is Carter and these gentlemen (he motioned to the other two) are my associates, Blue and Conrad." The rest of the introductions were made involving lots of cross-table hand-shaking. It got a bit confusing, fingers getting caught on fingers, hands bumping. Someone brought fresh coffee and butter croissants from the kitchen. Hugh passed the paper bag around the circle, and each of us Conspirators looked inside.

"Well . . . that . . . is . . . certainly . . . an . . . impressive . . . bag . . . of . . . money," Jimmy said. "Are . . . those . . . all . . . hundreds? Oh . . . wait . . . I . . . see . . . some . . . fifties . . . too."

"Jimmy, there's ten thousand in there," Carter said, "and I'm certain this honest crew," – his eyes swept the circle – "will put it to good use." We all nodded vigorously, still not quite believing this was happening. He took a sip of his coffee and slid his sunglasses onto the top of his head. His eyes were green and totally bloodshot. It was like looking at a stoplight stuck on stop and go at the same time.

"We heard about what you – what do you call yourselves? a conspiracy? – what you all were doing up here in Atlanta. Takes courage to try this in the middle of a city. I mean, yeah, Max Yasgur's farm was one thing, lots of room, no traffic, but, right in the middle of Atlanta? That's really cool. We also admire the fact that you're sharing the profits with two counter-culture groups. And, since profit couldn't be a motive, obviously, not at two bucks a ticket, we figured you people were either insane or righteous. We settled on righteous."

"See . . . that's . . . what . . . I . . . said . . . too . . . the . . . righteous . . . part," Jimmy chimed in, slowly, like funeral cymbals in a Krishna temple.

Carter continued. "We put the Gainesville Dealers' Association together for similar reasons. We wanted to provide positive energy and financial assistance when and where we could. You know, that whole Hippie mind-set. We were accumulating so much cash, bales of it," – a couple of us quietly coughed at the word 'bales' – "and, obviously we couldn't bank it, so we decided to spread the wealth, so to speak. Half of all the profit we made went to projects we thought would benefit as many people as possible, or to families who were in desperate situations that only money could solve."

"Half?" Hugh asked.

"Yes. The other half we're using to buy an island in the Caribbean where we're going to retire when we all turn forty, provided we don't wind up spending our lives in federal prison or getting wasted by the Mexican pot cartel. The Mexicans don't like the competition and they damn sure don't like our attitude. Anyway, that's the plan." The conversations droned on. Carter was a talker and a good story teller. Blue and Conrad, not so much. Muscles don't talk. They flex.

Finally, the meeting was ending. Handshakes all around again, promises to show up at the concert, incognito, of course, if they could.

"One last thing we're curious about," Carter said as he was settling himself behind the wheel of the gleaming Staff Car. "How have you gotten this far with this project of yours? I would think the City of Atlanta wouldn't be happy to see this come off. Rock and roll and crowds of freaks and drugs and traffic tie-ups. How'd you do it?"

"Well," I answered, "we made the City our co-sponsors. All the ads now say it's a co-production of the City and the Atlanta Rock Conspiracy. We had some help on the inside, in the Mayor's office."

Carter started laughing. "Are you going to add our name now, too? Make it a co-production of the City of Atlanta and an association of Florida-based pot dealers? That's what it actually is, right? What a fucking righteous deal! Atlanta and an association of drug dealers! Working together to bring rock and roll to the people! Jesus, let's hope they don't discover who they're working with until your gig is over! Good luck, guys!" And, off they went, Carter's laughter ricocheting off the trees that lined Jimmy's driveway as they drove away. Like I said: It was definitely a moment.

Our stage crew – the roadies, if we had been on the road – was run by one Mr. Dog, a wiry Southern boy who said he loved his Copenhagen snuff almost as much as he loved Jesus. Mr. Dog had worked for just about every Southern rock band touring in the early 70s and he knew his business. His job was to get the bands onstage as quickly as humanly possible, let them do their sound checks, *("Test, test! One, two, one two. Can I get a little more volume on the number two amp? Check. Check. One, two . . .)* and into their set. Once finished, after the band's encore and the applause was dying, Mr. Dog and his crew had no more than ten minutes to get that band offstage, without damaging any of their equipment or instruments, and move the next band onstage and set up the same as the previous band. It was a marvel to watch. I'm sure Mr. Dog knew nothing about "motion efficiency," but he could have written a training manual on the subject. His five-man crew all looked like their pictures were on wanted posters in various Post Offices across the South. But, like Mr. Dog, they were fast, efficient, and only paused to drink another beer or honk up another line of coke. Michael had an excellent coke connection and made sure Mr.

Dog's crew was well taken care of.

Concert day arrived. Sunday, April 20, 1975. The Conspiracy met in one of the amphitheater's back-stage dressing rooms for a final meeting and a round of self-congratulation for what we had accomplished. Anything could happen, of course, during the concert that might result in a monumental fuck-up, but we had faith and we were, as Jimmy kept reminding us, "righteous." Michael brought out a small paper bag, about the size of a lunch bag, and dumped the contents onto one of the dressing tables. A mound of pale pink powder studded with chunks of pale pink rocks tumbled onto the table. We all stopped whatever we were doing and stared. *Holy Mother of God!* Peruvian Pink! Right there in front of us! Jack was so overcome his legs started to buckle. In a show of absolute brotherhood (we had declared Katy an honorary man for the duration of the concert, to which she had said "get fucking real, boys") we gathered around the table and, altogether, bent over, placed our Krystal hamburger joint straws into the mound and honked up as much as we thought we could handle without dying. After the initial power rush and nose numbing it was bliss. At that precise moment, when all of us around that table were levitating and feeling pure joy, the dressing room door opened and in stepped Sgt. Luther Doolittle, the head of the police detail the city insisted we have on hand during the concert. The good sergeant had reached a reasonable agreement with us in the early stages of our planning. He would restrain his posse from making any reefer arrests inside the amphitheater unless he saw blatant dealing. We all knew people would be smoking weed and swallowing purple micro-dots and since the venue held seven thousand people, it would be impossible to arrest everybody. So, in the interest of peace, love, and harmony, no arrests. However, that didn't include the drug tableau Sgt. Doolittle had just walked in on. Everything stopped, frozen, including time, which is a weird warp in the universe when you've just sucked up a line of Peruvian Pink.

He hesitated, looked at the circle of rock and roll freaks bent over the table, looked at the table, paused a very long second, and then said, "Have a good concert, boys." He then turned around and walked out the door. God bless you, Sgt. Doolittle, wherever you are. So, in addition to the rapid, celestial heartbeat that occurs when coke of this purity is inhaled, we had the added thrill of a powerful adrenaline jolt, a twofer.

Mr. Dog came to the door and said it was time to open the amphitheater gates. The crowd lined up outside was growing and the opening act was still an hour away. We told Mr. Dog to go ahead and open them. The ticket sellers and ticket takers got into their places just inside the two gates we had unchained. We had a third volunteer standing at each gate with a hand-held counter, whose job it was to let us know how many people eventually came in. Very quickly the combined numbers reached 500; then 1,000; then 1,500; then 3,000, 4,000, 5,000, 8,000. An hour until showtime and the amphitheater was packed. Every seat was taken. People were sitting in the aisles, on the stone terraces that served as seating, and on the grassy banks inside the venue. And, thousands more were gathering in the park outside, and in the streets surrounding the park until, eventually, we heard a news flash on one of the rock stations that said to avoid the area of Chastain Park and the streets on the north side of the city because something had happened – a bomb? a plane crash? a huge fire? – that was causing a massive traffic jam with gridlock miles away from the park and nobody seemed to know what the fuck was happening on this otherwise normal Sunday here in the Buckle of the Bible Belt.

Then came the *"thwip-thwip-thwip"* of the television news helicopters overhead, getting louder as they approached the air-space over Chastain. It was madness. The arc of Atlanta's history was bending towards our rock and roll concert. Who knew it would be this much fun, this crazy?

With the crowd swelling and the ticket-takers unable to keep up with the flow, we followed the Woodstock model and declared the event a free concert. All the gates were unchained and opened. But, it made no difference. The place was packed, jammed, flooded with rock and rollers, hippies, people of all ages, colors, and stages of high expectation – emphasis on high. It was glorious. Mr. Dog materialized and shouted in my ear, "We gotta start the music, dude! This is gettin' outta hand!" And, so we did. An hour earlier than our agreement with the city stated, but, what? They were going to complain? Way too late for that.

Marshgrass opened it up with electric mountain music – a ten-person ensemble of wild banjos, electric fiddles, a dobro, acoustic and electric guitars, amplified harmonicas - that turned the crowd into a massive, stomping, clapping, audience who knew this was going to be an excellent day. And, it was. From the first act on, through the Southern rock of Carrie Nation and EQT; the wild theatrics of the Jive Ass Jug Band; the Dead-influenced Rock Mountain; the yeasty, Bread-like Warm; the roots music mystery of Rev. Pearly Brown, born before the beginning of the first world war; Darryl Rhoades and the Ha-Ha Vishnu Orchestra convincing half the audience (the half that was really high) it was 1967 not 1975, and we were all in the Haight, not Atlanta; Flood's Dark Side of the Moon-ish mind-freeing psychedelic riffs; and finally to Rita Godfrey's bluesy set that brought the concert to a close at midnight, it was all perfectly executed. No problems, no sound fuck-ups, the light show was spectacular and got several concert-goers, already tripping to the max, right to the edge of a full-blown break with reality. We gave them valium to calm them down and let them know that, no, that was not God approaching on a galloping, silver horse, its nostrils snorting fire and angels. It was a street-light outside the amphitheater. And, incredibly, there was only one arrest the entire day. One. And, that was a woman beating up her boyfriend for not sharing a strip of blotter acid she had brought to the concert to ensure a proper lift-off. He had swallowed the whole thing. We heard she was released later that afternoon after it became apparent the boyfriend was too fucked up to press charges.

It was 2AM. The bands had packed up and were gone. The massive screens on which The Wizard had projected a light show that had people shouting, *"Dave! What are you doing, Dave! I can feel it, Dave! Stop, Dave!"* had been taken down and packed away. Flood's sound system, that had provided all the gig's performers with crystal-clear thunder, had been loaded onto a Ryder truck and driven off into the night. A crew from the city's Department of Public Works was cleaning up the debris left by thousands of concert-goers. And, we, The Atlanta Rock Conspiracy, were momentarily at a place where utter exhaustion, various degrees of drug hangovers, relief that the event was over, and pure happiness of a sort I've seldom known since, all intersected at this falling-down amphitheater that we and thousands of rock fans had flooded with pure energy for ten hours. It was a good, no, it was an awesome feeling.

The next morning, we got together at the Bistro for a post-mortem on what we had successfully produced and where we were going next with the Conspiracy. The immediate consensus was to strike again, to do another concert that would establish the ARC as a radical production company that could work successfully and independently of the major concert promoters not just in Atlanta, but, the entire Southeast. The discussion droned on for hours and, as I listened, it began to come clear that something had changed since those first meetings in my apartment, a dramatic change that was trying to take the ARC to an entirely different level. It was head-spinning. The discussion turned to serious talk about booking major acts: David Bowie, Led Zepplin, Santana. Crazy talk. Total bullshit. What was happening? Where did our radical little organization suddenly disappear to? And why, the insane conversation continued, stop with groups like the Zepplin? How about a Beatles reunion? Someone eventually would pull it together! It would be historic! they were saying. We could do it! they insisted. We are righteous! they repeated over and over. And, a venue for such an historic moment? Atlanta Braves Stadium! Of course! It could hold 60 thousand people, maybe 70 thousand if we added extra seating on the field! Yes! Fuck yes! We are invincible! We are the Atlanta Rock Conspiracy!!

I had to leave. The discussion had gotten bonkers. Ego and greed were loose in the Bistro.

I drove to my apartment where it all had begun. My head was spinning. Tears were sliding down my cheeks. I went back and forth between complete shock that my co-Conspirators

147

had become delusional, and anger that the group had lost their fucking minds. All of them at the same time! I sat there for hours, aware the day was slowly dissolving, which was exactly how I was feeling: like I was floating away. The phone rang. It was Katy. "Hey," she said, "what are you doing?"

"Sitting here."

"I have something to tell you. It's not good."

"Go ahead."

"The board just voted you out."

"What board?"

"The ARC board."

"For fuck's sake, Katy, we don't have a board. Remember? The whole idea was to stay away from the corporate bullshit. There is no board. You know that."

"Okay, look, I'm sorry this is happening. I voted to keep you on. But the rest of the guys decided they wanted to take a different path. You heard what they were talking about before you walked out."

"So, they decided to just fucking take what I put together?"

"I hate to tell you, but, yes. Michael showed up with a folder full of stock certificates he had printed up. The ARC is going public."

Stock certificates? What the fuck!? "Katy, you have to be kidding me. Going public? Jesus fucking Christ!"

"Do you want me to come over? Hold your hand? You sound a bit frayed around the edges."

"No. This is insane. I can't believe they did this. Tell you what, Katy. If you go back to the meeting, tell my former "righteous" partners I said I hope they all die in a fucking plane crash. What a bunch of shit."

"Jesus, Mike. You know you don't mean that. I know you're

angry, but you can't wish them all dead! That's crazy! Please get a grip."

We talked for a few more minutes, Katy trying to calm me, make me see none of this was all that important. She reminded me there were people starving in Bangladesh, for God's sake. Right.

We finally hung up. I got in the car and drove towards Stone Mountain, replaying the last three months – and yesterday's gig – over and over in my head. I had to go someplace where I could think. I was still shaking from Katy's call.

The drive to the Mountain was just long enough for me to calm down a bit. I knew I'd better take a Zen-like attitude about the whole thing or keel over with a heart attack, but what the fuck did I know about simply noticing something passing by – like putting together a rock concert, for example – without judging anything that had happened? Isn't that what Buddhists did? No judgement. About anything. Just acceptance.

By the time I got to the park's gate I realized overthinking all this bullshit was ridiculous. What is, is. As Siddhartha Gautama said, "We are shaped by our thoughts: we become what we think." There's definitely a warning there . . .

It had been one hell of an experience. I couldn't help smiling when I thought about how we pulled the whole thing together, especially the financing. The City of Atlanta, to this day, has no idea who one of their partners was for that one glorious day of rock and roll all those years ago: the Gainesville Dealers Association. Drug dealers and the administration of the capitol of The New South, Atlanta, bringing the raucous pleasure of rock and roll to the masses.

And, that was a real knee-slapper.

Chapter 13

Talk Radio

Fall, 1986. Atlanta. By now, I had been a radio talk show host for two years.

This was not a career I sought. It found me.

For nearly three years, beginning in 1983, I worked as a writer and occasional producer for CNN television. The idea of a 24-hour news network was considered ridiculous when founder Ted Turner first developed the concept. Part of the ridicule was Turner himself. Granted, he owned a television "superstation," one that could be picked up via cable across the country, and an outdoor advertising company he inherited when his father died. But Turner's broadcast experience was limited to televising Atlanta Braves (which he owned) baseball games and syndicated sitcom re-runs. Worse, he was a white Southern male who lived in Georgia, not in one of the two the broadcast centers of the universe, New York City and Los Angeles. What could he possibly know about television news that the experts didn't? As it turned out, just about everything.

I met him on one of his walks through CNN's first home, a

building built in the style of an antebellum mansion located not far from the city's center. He had the habit of occasionally strolling through the network's production and broadcast center - the "bullpen," - stopping at a writer's desk or a supervising editor's work station, to get a quick look at the next hour's broadcast. He didn't engage in idle conversation; no polite inquiries about the writer's spouse or the kids, if there were any. His questions were about the stories we were about to televise across the country and around the world, and why we, the writers and producers, considered them newsworthy. Turner believed – certainly in the early days of CNN – that news broadcasts should, must, be topic driven. To clutter the newscast with personalities, including those of the news-readers (anchors) would be to defeat the purpose of an all-news network, as well as being an insult to people depending on news outlets for needed information. To that end, those of us involved in the early years at CNN truly felt dedicated to getting the truth out. Or maybe it was just fear of pissing off Turner, the man named "The Mouth of the South" by some smart-ass Yankee sports writer

But . . . working at a 24-hour news channel was exhausting as well as, at times, overwhelming. In the beginning there had been no repeat newscasts, no re-broadcasts. A 24-hour news channel was just that. Show after show had to be written, edited, and then re-written if there was the slightest hint of a factual error or – god help us - political bias in the copy. We were there to write and produce and broadcast news and no mercy was offered to the employee who didn't have that clear understanding from the first day of his or her employment. And the unforgiving deity who watched over all of this, ready to lash any of us with a silent and invisible whip, was the God of Time, truly a merciless bastard. If a show was to begin at 8PM or 9PM or midnight or whatever, then that show would begin at 8PM or 9PM or midnight or whatever even if the world outside the CNN studios was engulfed in flames. The. Broadcast. Would. Be. Delivered. The God of Time was not to be denied. Ever. Employees who didn't understand this were quickly disappeared. Eventually, after a couple of intense and money-losing years in which attempts to maintain live newscasts 24/7 became untenable, it was decided the last show would end at 2:00 AM each morning and the building would be empty for the next three hours. Then the morning crews would arrive, the lights turned back on, and the process would begin again.

Because of the schedules and the intensity of covering worldwide events, most of them bloody and horrific, there were moments when the tension in the production studio was so thick it seemed to take on form and mass. Working under those conditions could lead to moments of desperation if, for example, during a momentary break and running to the john to pee and honk up a dot of coke, you found the bathroom stall was already occupied. Coffee and coke. (The powdery kind, not the kind where dozens of people stand on a verdant hillside and sing a song of love for our sisters and brothers.) For some of us that combination delivered the thrust needed to be the best damn news writers and producers in the universe! Or so we told ourselves.

One night, October 30, 1984, late, after the final newscast, I was tugging on my jacket ready to go to a late night Halloween party. Suddenly, all eight of the teletype machines in the bullpen went berserk. Bells ringing, printers clacking, a threatening signal that somewhere a catastrophe was unfolding in real time. Nuclear war? A massive earthquake? A rogue planet had invaded the solar system and was heading straight for Earth?

There were three of us left in the building: A supervising producer, the news anchor who had just finished the 1:30 AM newscast, and me. We all ran to the nearest teletype to see if the Russians had, in fact, launched a couple hundred nuclear-tipped missiles over the North Pole. The copy we ripped from the machine said Indira Gandhi had been assassinated. No nukes. No Commie annihilation coming our way. Just your run-of-the-mill assassination of a renowned head of state. Only, this was the leader of the second most populous country on earth. Stabbed to death with short swords wielded by two Sikh nationalists, one of whom was shot dead by security guards, the other, wounded, taken to hospital where he would have the best medical techniques and medicines in India, fully recover, and then executed for the gruesome murder.

While the bells kept frantically ringing the producer told our anchor guy to get back on the broadcast set while he turned the cameras on again and I wrote the story as quickly as I could. He also told me to find a Sikh. In Atlanta. At 2:00 AM. And, I did. I knew a man named Khalsa who owned a Sikh grocery store in one of the city's gentrifying neighborhoods. I woke him with a phone call and asked for comment about Gandhi's assassination. In his half-awake state I had to tell him several times I meant Indira now, and not *Bapu* decades ago.

I got the needed comment, our skeleton staff got the story out to the world beyond India, and an hour later, still twitching from the mad adrenaline rush, an occurrence that had been happening with alarming regularity lately, I realized it was time to find a different career, one that was not quite so potentially stroke-inducing.

That different career turned out to be talk radio.

My good friend Teresa was the office manager at WCNN – a local talk station with absolutely no connection whatsoever to CNN television. The owner had been close to the Turner family and, to raise the station's profile in Atlanta, got Ted's permission to use those magic call letters. Teresa said I should talk to the station manager. She knew I was burned out on the insane pressure that saturated CNN, and her boss was looking for someone to host a Saturday afternoon show focusing on local politics.

"You should do this, Mike. It's ready-made for a political junkie like you. And it's only two hours a week. How's that for low pressure?"

"Yeah, but I know nothing about radio, T," I answered.

"What's to know? You get on the air and rant. I know your rants. You'd be perfect. You can work out all that frustration, all that repressed masculine rage, right? And, a chance to unleash your inner motor-mouth. Is that not perfect?"

Teresa was an Atlanta actor and one of my housemates. A small group of us – a couple of actors, a photographer, a writer, a psychology student, and anyone else who applied when we had an occasional opening – had, a few years earlier, pooled our minimal resources to come up with a down payment and, selecting one of us to apply for the mortgage financing (a guy who had been in the Navy just long enough to qualify for a VA loan) bought a rambling house in an area of the city soon to experience yuppie rehabilitation. We were not the yuppies; we were among the neighborhood's first *artistes*, thank you very much, who eventually rode a wave of creativity that crested when the film industry realized there was talent in parts of the country other than California or New York. Atlanta, for example.

"Can you set up a meeting?" I asked Teresa.

"Already have. Tomorrow at two o'clock. I knew you'd want to do this, so I went ahead and made your appointment. You pissed because I didn't ask first?" She knew I wasn't. We had just shared a rather intense summer and, for a while, knew each other's thoughts before they were spoken.

"I'll be there. And, thanks. One more week at CNN and you'll have to come visit me on Sunday afternoons at Georgia Regional Hospital."

"I know. And visiting a mental facility always makes me nervous."

The interview went well, and he day after, I was offered the position. Saturdays, 2PM until 4PM, with the possibility of more hours if I could show management I knew what I was doing. Only one small catch: For the time being, there was no pay. The station was struggling, trying to compete in a market that was the home to dozens of radio stations including a couple of so-called heritage stations, one of which had been on the air since Jesus was a teenager. Most of Atlanta's radio advertising dollars went to those two. WCNN was the perfect place to learn the art and the insanity of political talk. The station had a relatively small listener base, so my factual errors and verbal fuck-ups could float off into the ozone with no one noticing. Perfect.

Because of my political point of view, it didn't take long to realize I was going to be swimming upstream, so to speak. During my interview, I was asked about my politics, which at the time were liberal-left. "Well, I'm a Conservative," the manager said, "so we should get along just fine." That didn't make a whole lot of sense, but, I let it go.

Atlanta's commercial talk-radio stations were saturated with right-wingers who were dedicated to protecting the ultra-Conservative lies and insanity that were codified in the South before radio was invented. For example:

First, in the South, Jesus is Lord! There is no god but God and Jesus is one-third of his name. You're a sinner and you must be "born again," in addition to being washed in the sticky blood of The Lamb. And, if you don't accept that? Well, then, you will roast in Hell for all eternity while spiders, scorpions, and snakes tear at your flesh and Satan sits smiling down from his throne of grinning skulls, except for those moments when he comes down to piss into one of your eye sockets.

Second: All women are temptresses and must be kept under control or their insane sexual urges will explode and they will tear through the cities and towns forcing every man they see to have animal sex with them right then and there in the street, and if a pregnancy results these licentious bitches will immediately try to destroy the precious little baby peacefully asleep in their wombs, surrounded by the everlasting love of the afore-mentioned Jesus.

Third: Actual, live children, the white ones, are nasty little un-churched creatures who, as they grow into their teen years, very quickly decide that rather than attending Sunday School and learning about Jesus they'd rather do drugs, fornicate in the back seat of their parents' car, lie, join gangs, date a colored person, or worse, start questioning the church's ridiculous superstitions, insane zombie tales, adulterous and incestuous sex, mass murder, wholesale destruction of innocent tribes who got in the way of God's designated hitters, and all the truly sick bullshit to be found in the most violent and pornographic book ever written, the Bible.

Fourth: Beware of the colored races. They are, um, not like us. Not in the least. They are all Liberals. They steal whenever they have the chance; they will stop whatever they're doing and start jerking and shaking whenever they hear drums; they sell drugs; they use drugs; their music will lead happy, white, Christian young ladies down dark hallways where they will be forced to have sex with large black men who have huge penises – much bigger than Dad's and, therefore, sinful and in violation of nature, and the innocent girls, now debauched and ruined, will eventually lose their minds, and end their lives walking the streets of the city selling their bodies for food and a furnished room somewhere.

Last, and most important: Jesus was not a short, dark-skinned, curly-haired Palestinian Jew who worked as a carpenter and part-time rabbi when he wasn't trying to get people to show each other respect and treat each other with kindness. No, not at all. He was a tall, blond, white Conservative Republican who looked Norwegian and spoke American English and was repulsed by homosexuals and any sort of birth control, which really wasn't birth control at all, but, rather, pregnancy control. With pregnancy control available women could have as much sex as men and adopt the same attitudes about doing so. Which was: Fuck 'em all! The long, the short, and the tall! Any depiction of the Christian Savior to the contrary was blasphemous. Oh, and this blond Messiah had no major issues with war, poverty, diseases, hunger, and/or death. It was all part of "God's plan." Full stop.

And, these were the beliefs buttressed by the *least* crazy right-wing talk radio glue-head listeners. Eventually, like within a week of my starting, the real maniacs started calling the station and demanding they rid Atlanta's airwaves of this Communist, gay-loving, liberal (me) who was surely having an affair with a sultry Negro woman who was getting massive monthly welfare checks that she then used to buy drugs which were stashed in the trunk of her shiny, new Cadillac until she sold them to innocent white children from the suburbs. And, where did this new program host come from anyway? He certainly wasn't from around here. That "from around here" determinant is very important in the South. In fact, it's the second most asked question when two people meet for the first time, the first being, "what church do you attend?" And, if you are not "churched" you make some shit up, like, "uh . . . First Baptist," hoping your interrogator is a member of some church other than First Baptist because every city, town, village, and country crossroads in the South has a First Baptist. And a First Methodist. And a First Presbyterian. And on through the denominational line-up of the Reformation. Catholics? Shush, now.

So, it was in that environment that I began my talk radio career. And, I was well prepared for the onslaught of religious freaks who I knew would find my presence a sure sign of the advent of the anti-Christ. My Italian grandparents, in their frantic need to fully assimilate into the New World, had shed their Catholicism and joined a Baptist church in Ohio. Grandma was determined to be the best Christian ever, maybe to ease the guilt of her conversion to Protestantism. Attending church was an absolute requirement for anyone living in or visiting her home. Perhaps because I spent most of my summers with her until I was eleven years old, I became a "project."

Of her 13 grandchildren, I was the one she decided she would make damn certain was "saved," that I would avoid the "lake of fire," that terrifying pit of unspeakable torture and anguish deep in the bowels of Hell that was waiting for all sinners and non-Christians. And, it didn't matter whether one lived a life free from sin or not. Grandma believed the admonition found in the first book of Paul's letters to the church at Ephesus: "By grace are you saved, not of works, lest any man should boast." Granted, that's a rough translation of the original Aramaic, but the meaning was clear: If, as an example, you were a Jew there was no way you were going to Heaven just for, say, developing a vaccine that saved millions of lives from the suffering and painful death caused by some hideous disease, or bringing an end to famine, or finding a way to end all wars, or anything else that would be considered amazing and wondrous and beautiful and glorious. Hell no. Heaven was an exclusive celestial resort reserved for Christians, even though Jesus himself was a Jew. Apparently, he converted.

Furthermore, everybody, was a sinner. You couldn't escape it. You were born a sinner, totally fucked and condemned even as you were drawing in your very first gasping breath after living inside a soft, pitch-dark waterbed for nine months. And, all the terrible shit that had ever happened, or would eventually happen, was because Eve had decided it was better to know than to be ignorant and had snatched a pomegranate from the Tree of Life, gobbled it down, and suddenly realized she was naked. Such a cosmic crime. Apparently, the worst ever committed.

There was only one way out, one path to "salvation" – the Christian term for avoiding the Hell Beasts waiting to torture you for eternity. And, that was to be born again. When I was a kid, I tried to imagine what that meant, how that was handled, and I spent many restless and freaked-out nights lying in bed, unable to sleep, horrified at the thought of being stuffed back into my mother's insides and then popped out again. That's some heavy shit for a kid to worry about.

And, the anxiety increased exponentially when grandma tried to explain, if that's the correct word, that, no, it wasn't a physical birth the church was talking about, it was . . . something else. Something even scarier because she couldn't really explain the process. Magic? Ghosts? Belief? "You have to learn to have faith," she would tell me. What was that and how did I learn it? I was still having a tough time trying to learn how to ride my bike. However, Grandma's dedication to my salvation did tuck away in my memory an endless supply of verses, stories, predictions, and threats – all from the Bible. And, let us not forget Wednesday night prayer meeting.

My grandparents conversion after they arrived in the States was an attempt to minimize their being Italian in a small Ohio city shortly after the turn of the 20th century. There was always the suspicion they might be Anarchists, ready to set off the bombs they probably had already planted in the town square when the signal came from headquarters somewhere in Rome. Why add the threat of being Papists, too? Those worshippers of graven images, whose priests made weird hand motions and chanted in an occult language not at all like the English Jesus surely spoke. Foreigners only caused trouble. Especially the non-white foreigners, Italians being the perfect example. Silvia, for instance. Once, she told me how embarrassed she felt when one of her classmates asked, "Does your dad carry a knife?"

"No," she answered. "Why do you think my dad carries a knife?"

"Cuz my pop says all Dagoes carry knives!"

"My dad's not a Dago."

"Yes, he is!"

"No, he isn't and that's a bad word. I'm gonna tell the teacher you said it and you'll probably be expelled!"

"And you're one, too."

"No, I'm not!"

"Are too! Dago!"

At which point Silvia would start crying, feeling the sting of being insulted for her skin color, for being a Dago, for being foreign. In her eighth-grade class photograph she is at once noticeable. She's standing a few inches away from the other students, her dark skin made darker by the white graduation dress. There she was, the single "colored" girl in the school.

Silvia's parents were church-goers. Twice on Sundays and prayer meeting every Wednesday night. During my summer visits the mid-week trips to Calvary Baptist Church gave me a chance to watch people praying with a fervency that I couldn't help but marvel at. Did they really believe some Sky Spook was listening to them, with their shouting and trembling? Did they really expect the Hairy Thunderer to drop whatever He was doing, wherever He was doing it, maybe in Africa where He was really busy healing all those millions of lepers, or infecting millions more depending on his mood at the moment, and then making sure everybody had enough to eat, drop it all and rush halfway around the world to Findlay, Ohio, find the Calvary Baptist Church, and seriously listen to this hysteria? Yeah, they did.

The prayer meetings took place in one of the church's dusty, hot, upper rooms. I was the only kid there and while the group of adults each took his or her turn, on their knees, their backs to the middle of the prayer circle, hands folded on the wooden seats of the ladder-back chairs, I watched the dust motes floating in the early evening sunlight that filtered into the room through the stained, grimy windows. Not stained-glass windows. That was for wealthy congregations, like Catholics. Calvary Baptist windows were just stained, mostly with bird shit.

They prayed for everything: Their sick relatives, the recently dead, the soon-to-be dead, the souls lost to alcohol, the non-believers, President Truman, themselves. On and on it went, each one in turn. When it came my grandparents' turn, there was no loud wailing, no pleading exhortations, no tears. Angelo and Laura made quiet prayers. God forbid, so to speak, they would make a spectacle of themselves, even in this moldy upper room with a circle of their co-religionists. And, they were quick. No extraneous bullshit like praying for President Truman. Just hit the high spots: relatives, health issues, the drunks, the unsaved and on to the Amen.

I never told Laura I was an atheist, that I knew there was no such thing as god, or heaven, or angels, or answered prayers. I knew these things because if there was a god how could he be so fucking cruel? Wars, famines, diseases, hatred, death, all of it could have been stopped with the wave of his heavenly hand. But, no. And, on a lower level, why would god allow Joe to beat us kids and Silvia simply because he was insane? I loved my grandma, for sure, but, her *god*? No way. It was all bullshit and I wanted to tell her that even though I knew she wouldn't have listened and probably would have taken one of her mulberry-bush switches and whipped the devil out of me. I hope she was welcomed with angels strumming harps of gold when she arrived at the gates to her heaven.

Chapter 14

Naked

The topic my first day as a talk show host concerned the poisonous, acidic discharges from a company that made batteries for cars and trucks. The manufacturing plant sat on the banks of a nearby lake, created in the 1950s by the U.S. Army Corp of Engineers. The lake's original purpose was to bring hydroelectric power and water to metro Atlanta. Now, families from four states used the lake for recreation. They swam there; they picnicked there; they went boating and water skiing; they fished; they had fun. The battery maker didn't give a shit about any of that. If there were toxic chemicals and heavy metals that had to be disposed, well, isn't that why lakes and streams and rivers exist? To hide the by-products that were part of the manufacturing process? And, anyway, who would ever know? The discharge would be at night, in the still darkness, the only sound the gentle flow of poison flowing into the lake. Fish don't scream when sulphuric acid is eating holes in their bodies.

Well, fuck no to all that! I, the newly christened Caped Crusader of Atlanta talk radio, would get on these environmental criminals like white on rice! And, with that thought bouncing around inside my head, I sat down behind the microphone, ready for battle. There was a potential audience of several million people within the broadcast area of the station. However, nearly all of them were focused on the Georgia, Arkansas football game in the Liberty Bowl. Who the hell wanted to hear about battery acid? The Bulldogs were beating the Razorbacks! Everything else was either secondary or totally inconsequential. Sundays in Georgia may belong to Jesus, but Autumn Saturdays are owned by the University of Georgia's football team. Amen and amen.

After my opening 10-minute rant about the evil and soulless capitalists who owned the battery factory and who were without remorse as they polluted and destroyed one of the pristine recreation areas in the Southeast, I opened the phone lines for comments from the listeners. The first call was from a nice old lady who wanted to know if I was "saved." She said her name was Rose.

"Young man, are you saved? Do you know Jesus?"

"Excuse me . . .?"

"Have you found Jesus?"

"I didn't know he was lost . . . "

She let that slide. Or it just flew right by her.

"You're new at this radio station, aren't you. Are you saved? Do you know where you're going to spend eternity?"

"Uh . . . no, but what do you think about dumping battery acid into Lake Lanier?"

"You know, it says in the Bible that when He comes it'll be in the blinking of an eye."

"Yes, ma'm, that's pretty fast."

"Well, yes, it is, and you won't have time to repent when the

Trumpet of the Lord shall sound and time shall be no more. And that means all around the earth. There's no place you can hide."

"Okay . . . " I wanted to add the next line ". . . *and the roll is called up yonder I'll be there*" knowing I had lost control of the conversation, my first as a talk show host. It was embarrassing.

"Well, young man, what church do you worship at? Where do you go to church?"

"Uh . . ."

"You are churched, aren't you?"

The Program Director's Prime Directive when he hired me was never, never hang up on a caller. No matter how crazy I might think of what they were saying, hanging up on them was not allowed. Instead, try to win them over to my point of view; be sympathetic, understanding, and always polite.

"And here are three absolutes to file away as you begin this adventure," the PD had added with a mock serious tone to his voice. "One, always be truthful. Two, there will always be a gay man somewhere who wants to have your baby. And, three, I will always be listening."

Rose was getting on my nerves, "Well, Rose, I . . . actually . . . uh . . . well, it's like this . . ."

"You don't go to church, do you." It was a statement, not a question. "Well, then, are you prepared to spend eternity with the Devil? Do you want to burn in the Lake of Fire forever? And, what about your mother? I'm sure she didn't raise you so you could burn in the Lake of Fire now did she."

Well, at least Rose was talking about a lake. Different lake, but we were close to being on the same page. I decided to ease Rose back to wherever she came from when she decided to call

165

the program.

"Okay, Rose, you got me. Yes, I belong to a church. It's the Church of Wicca."

"Now, where is that? And, what is a Wicca? Is that part of the Southern Baptists?"

"No, ma'm, my church doesn't believe in a particular god. We love nature, the natural world, you know, trees and forest creatures, and we dance in the light of the moon. Do you like to dance, Rose?"

Her voice went from patronizing to threatening. "You don't believe in our Lord Jesus Christ?! You are nature worshippers?! Young man, you are in serious danger! The Devil is leading you! Darkness is about to envelop you! Your soul will shrivel and die, amen! Get down on your knees now and beg the Lord's mercy!"

"Uh . . . Rose, it's only half past two in the afternoon. It doesn't get dark until, what? seven, eight o'clock this time of year?"

I saw my producer pick up the "hot line," the studio phone that was used only if absolutely necessary and was the direct link to the PD. He listened for a moment, then hung up and waved to get my attention. He was making a cutting motion across his throat. I could read his lips: Hang up! Hang the fuck up! Get her OFF!

"Hey, Rose, I gotta go. I do appreciate your call. Take care, okay?"

"You are going straight to Hell, mister . . . "

We went to commercials.

"Well, that's a first," my producer said. "Boss man said tell Mike to hang up on this caller. Now."

Not even one day on the job and I'd caused the Program

Director to violate the Prime Directive. It was a sign.

Several months rolled by. I was learning the finer points of talk radio while firmly establishing myself as - depending on your political point of view - either the Atlanta radio market's sole Liberal maniac who had no business being on the air and should be removed immediately, or a blessing to the ever-expanding base of politically progressive activists who were determined to further the faltering human rights stance of a city that had, for the most part, avoided the ugliness and violence that had rotted the soul of so many Southern cities during the ending of Jim Crow laws and the beginning of the civil rights era. The names of the giants of the Civil Rights Movement will always be linked with Atlanta, starting, of course, with Dr. Martin Luther King, Jr.

I had moved from WCNN – and no pay – to the monster station of the Southeast (and a reasonable paycheck) WSB-AM. It was referred to as the "blowtorch" of the South because of the station's broadcast power, especially at night when the hundreds of daytime-only stations across fifteen states went off the air and a potential radio audience of millions was there for the picking. As far as hosting a talk radio program, I was a quick study. My time at CNN television had taught me how to do rapid but factual research on just about any topic that was considered politically controversial and, therefore, fodder for this rapidly changing medium in which I now found myself. And the relatively brief time I spent in theatre also was an asset in that I had learned that theatrical thing of "getting into character." The character I got into – or, more precisely, let emerge - each time I went on the air was a hard-core liberal who would tolerate zero right-wing verbal garbage. The getting-into-character thing happened when I

167

did a play in which my role required me to be completely naked. Completely.

For three years prior to my CNN fun, I had been part of a troupe of radical actors called The Southern Theatre Conspiracy. Such a group. We performed some traditional theatre – Shakespeare, Miguel Pinero, Arthur Schnitzer, Sam Shepard – and a few thoroughly outrageous company-developed offerings. My favorite original play was one written for the most part by the troupe's founder and artistic director, Eddie Lee. The title was "Spare Ribs." It was a feminist comedy about the creation of Woman as seen through the eyes of the first Man, God, and Satan. I was offered the role of Adam.

It was my first time performing as an honest-to-god actor, with a paying audience, publicity, the roar of the greasepaint, the smell of the crowd. There was one catch in my being Adam. Eddie knew I was a complete novice. I had joined the company to develop playwriting skills, not acting. Once in, however, the acting appeared to be easier than writing and considerably more fun so, I signed up for Acting 101 and scene study classes taught by Eddie' wife who ran the company's drama school. My prior stage experience began and ended with a 7th grade production of "Music Man." To Eddie, that was a bonus. I had no preconceptions of how to use the stage, no earlier training or experience that would have to be overcome for the part I was being offered. The catch? Adam, in a one-act that ran just under an hour, would be nude onstage during the entire performance. No scenery cover, no costume, nothing to hide behind except the make-up, the grease paint.

Of course Adam would be nude. Wasn't that a key element of this three-religion creation myth? Adam and Eve frolicked naked in the Garden until Eve took bad advice from a snake and ate a ripe fruit hanging from the Tree of Knowledge. Instantly, she and her male partner were condemned to death. In fact, every living thing was condemned to eventual death. And, that wasn't all because this particular god was the sort who was easily pissed and apparently very possessive of his precious little tree. So, not only was death introduced, this vindictive, psychotic god decided to curse all women in a singularly nasty way, all of them, including the billions who were not yet born. The curse would be forever. The Heavenly Bully told Eve that henceforth she and her female descendants would bleed every month and be unclean and give birth in extreme pain and some of them would die in the process. How's that for celestial insanity? And all because of Eve's easily understood curiosity. Oh, and the ladies wouldn't get the right to vote for millennia. And, they'd have to deal with unequal pay for the same work as men, once work for pay had been invented. All for the sin of taking a bite out of a pomegranate? What a load of bullshit. But, that load became the foundational creation myth of three religions, all three of which have been trying to destroy each other since they realized they had to share their god. And giving him three different names didn't ease the tension. It just made matters worse.

But, the play. Adam. Nudity. I knew this was going to be the sort of experience that I'd either get through successfully or crash and burn in the most embarrassing and permanently damaging way possible. An actor portraying the Biblical first man would look like some sort of coward, a sad amateur, an inauthentic *poseur*, if he didn't play Adam naked, so there was no way to compromise. Even a strategically placed leaf was out of the question. I talked it over with my therapist who, herself, had once been active in theatre.

"What are you most concerned about?" she asked during a session devoted to the terror of being nude in front of a crowd of people.

"Being nude in front of a crowd of people," I answered.

"Your concern is perfectly normal, unless you're a nudist," she said in that endearing way therapists have of agreeing with just about anything the client says. "But, you're an actor. At least right now you're an actor. So, why let this cause you any anxiety?"

What? Wasn't that obvious? One of the most upsetting – and common – dreams people share is being in a crowd or the produce section of the grocery store or on a bus and suddenly one's clothes disappear.

"Have you spent any time in your acting classes discussing getting into character?"

"A bit, yes."

"Well, there you go. You've got to *become* Adam before you walk out onto the stage."

Oh, of course. Become Adam. Just do it. Then everything will be stress-free and calm, and I'll have an exciting time being naked on stage for almost an hour. Except, of course, that was bullshit for a novice like me. So, the answer was simple: Do some basic research. Talk with some of Atlanta's experienced male actors. Ask them how to handle nudity onstage. That's the ticket. But, surprise! surprise! not a single Atlanta actor, male or female, had ever performed fully nude on an Atlanta stage. Or anywhere for that matter. I was not in New York City where challenging roles such as being called upon to perform naked were common, certainly more so than here in the buckle of the Bible Belt. It was time to talk once again with my therapist.

Meanwhile, the City Attorney heard of our upcoming performances and sent a letter to Eddie stating that such a horror as a naked person – especially a man, with his. . . *thing* exposed onstage would simply not be tolerated. Not in his city. In fact, if the performance went forward as scheduled Eddie, as the owner of the theatre and I, as the obscene performer, would both be arrested for offending public decency. It was time to bring in some reinforcements. Eddie enlisted the assistance of a local minister – whose church catered primarily to gay men – and a couple of local attorneys whose specialty was protecting the First Amendment. The preacher assured the City Attorney that the play was Biblical. Weren't Adam and Eve both comfortably naked until The Fall? Did the Attorney want to be accused of discrimination against religion as well as restricting protected speech?

Well, put that way the City Attorney backed off. With one warning: Even a hint of sexual reference or sexuality in general would be dealt with severely. In other words, jail. The message was simple: go ahead and have your naked play but we'll be watching. And God help all us degenerate actors if undue attention – any attention – was paid to someone's penis, which, by process of elimination among the other cast members, meant mine.

The next few weeks were spent in rehearsal and since this was a company-developed play the dialogue and blocking were subject to change daily, depending on input from us actors. Since Adam's lines were minimal I used the rehearsals to "become" Adam. I tried to get into character with all the fervor of someone trying to avoid the worst possible thing other than a terminal disease. And, surprise! slowly I was getting there. During rehearsals the other actors – all female, even the God character, and the several women who had the roles of Satan's experiments with providing Adam a suitable woman, *i.e* the Mother, the Whore, the Virgin, the Comforter – were clothed while I frolicked around the stage naked. Eddie wanted me to become comfortable with the other actors first, then deal with the terror of a live audience. To this day I am grateful that during rehearsals my fellow actors didn't get into dick jokes and snarky comments about "shrinkage."

Opening night arrived. We actors were all backstage applying makeup – for me, lots of it - when Eddie came in with word that the City Attorney had an observer in the audience with an arrest warrant, blank where names could be filled in. The scary warrant with its empty spaces reminded us yet again that the theatre would be closed if there was any bullshit about the true nature of the play. It was either Biblical or pornographic. No middle ground. The cast had a good laugh and started doing obscene hip thrusts and whispering, "Fuck me, Adam! Oh, baby. Do me." No time, girls. Maybe later. Then I noticed something completely unacceptable: my little friend had developed its own stage fright and, while trying to force its way up into my body cavity, had shrunk to the size of a small mushroom, one of those little white ones that grow best on the exposed roots of trees. *Oh, no.* I now had only minutes before the light cues would open the play and I was to be lying prone on the stage while God finished creating me. Not with this shrunken dick! No way in hell I was going to be center stage, lights coming up, a full house of anticipatory play-goers and me with a teeny-weenie wiener. I knew what to do: don't panic! Just tug on it, stretch it, pull it up to normal size. I was in a corner of the darkened backstage doing exactly that when Sue, the actor playing God, crept by, getting into position for her entrance, and when she saw what I was doing she whispered, way too loud for backstage chatter, *"What are you doing? You can't do that here! You're about to take your place!"*

"I'm not doing what you think, for godssake!" was all I could think to answer, also in a whisper and also way too loud for a small theatre with a full house. Later, at the opening night party, a friend said the whispers could be heard all the way to the cheap seats in the back row. "What *were* you doing?" was the first thing she asked. I winked at her and went to get another drink.

We weren't arrested. The play was a hit. In the middle of that first performance the official observer left, either because he realized the play was, in fact, not obscene or possibly because he got bored. Or, maybe unacceptably excited. Whatever, he split. The production ran for the scheduled six weeks, four performances a week, and when it ended I knew two things: First, I would never again have that panicky dream of being naked in public, and second, I had developed a dedicated following of gay men who came to see performance after performance, which increased the play's receipts dramatically, bless their hearts. Thanks, boys.

Alas, after the close contact of six weeks of performing – and three weeks of daily rehearsals prior to that - I realized theatre people were way too crazy for me. Fun, yes. But, too close to emotional derangement. Not that emotional derangement is necessarily a bad thing. In fact, for most actors, it's a requirement. For me, however, that sort of crazy was a condition I spent my entire life trying to avoid. Why take the chance of a full break with reality that can come when it's necessary – as it is in theatre – to "become" a different person with a completely different personality and, in some roles, a completely different physical appearance. Too risky, if you teeter along the edge of chaos in real life. As my therapist reminded me often during 20-plus years of therapy, "Tread lightly. We all are just one shrieking episode away from total psychological disintegration," which was excellent advice and a perfectly suitable suggestion for anyone who wants to make it through this life with the least amount of damage and get on to the next one. And that was part of her charm. She offered all sorts of insightful shit just like that. Shrieking episode, indeed.

Chapter 15

Federal Prison

By this point in my nascent radio career, I had spent months trying to develop an attitude less about my shock at the bigotry and ignorance of some of the callers, and more about adopting an attitude of uncritical persuasion, especially with the geeks who called the station with their complaints that I was "un-American" and certainly not a Christian. That included the people who were fleeing the city for the suburbs to escape the racist and asinine belief of an imminent break-down of civil order. The rise of Atlanta's African-American business and political class and the growing influx of black people moving to the city from other parts of the country was a further cause of the white fear and the insistence on keeping "white" things white, including the radio station most of them had grown up listening to, the one on which I now had a nightly, three-hour program. Suddenly, the shoe of Atlanta's political power, so to speak, was being put on the other foot and a lot of whites didn't want to risk having it planted firmly up their asses. Southern white privilege, which had been the rule for generations, was changing, dissolving. And the correct perception that I was an advocate of equality of opportunity as well as justice, was seriously pissing off the city's cultural and social old guard.

The topics available for discussion were in abundance. It was the mid-80s, Reagan was nearing the mid-point of his second term as president and every day brought news of yet another crime against humanity specifically, and crimes against the American people generally, committed by key members of his administration. Predatory capitalism and its partner political authoritarianism were engulfing not just the U.S, but also the rest of the world. It was becoming overwhelming. If you were a radio talk show host with a cynical yet still liberal attitude, the developing global hysteria and the crimes of the Reaganites were welcome fodder for the next show. And the one after that. And, on and on. It was a time of political deceit at the highest levels of government, a time saturated with lies and half-truths from media fascists, poison that was slowly being absorbed into the bloodstream of America courtesy of a new class of right-wing propagandists: It was The Age of Limbaugh.

As an example of the chaos developing, in part because of the wholly irrational fear of Communism, April, 1980, saw the beginning of the Mariel boatlift, the mass migration of tens of thousands of people who wanted to leave Cuba for the U.S. The Cuban leader, Fidel Castro, saw an opportunity to rid his island country of people he considered to be less than enthusiastic for *la Revolution* that in 1959, after five years of guerilla warfare, had rid Cuba of the dictator Fulgencio Batista who had been enthusiastically supported by both the U.S. government and the Mafia. Batista had been good for business, the sort of business both the U.S government and the Mafia found profitable.

By October, 1980, the boatlift was ended by an agreement between the Cuban and U.S. leadership after more than 125,000 Cubans had reached Florida. Among those immigrants, or political refugees, depending on one's political point of view, were people Castro considered to be criminals, along with hundreds of people U.S. media insisted were from the country's mental hospitals. While the vast majority of those coming to the U.S. during the boatlift were assimilated and blended into their new country with very little effort, there were those who were locked up for various reasons at various detention centers around the country, including the Federal Penitentiary in Atlanta. Their chances for release were minimal because no one in the then new U.S. government of Ronald Reagan was clear on what to do, what the legal obligations were, or even who was to oversee the situation. The frozen state of affairs dragged on. A new administration came to power and in November, 1987, President George H. W. Bush unexpectedly announced an agreement with Cuba that would permit the repatriation – much of it forced – of up to 2,500 Cuban nationals. When the agreement became public, the Cubans being held in the Atlanta Penitentiary, who had no desire to return to Cuba, rioted and seized control of the prison. For eleven days the uprising continued. The inmates were desperate. They knew what awaited them if they went back. They insisted on the freedom they had been promised when they left Cuba.

In the middle of this potentially explosive situation, a message was left on my answering machine from one of the American human rights attorneys who were voluntarily representing the prisoners. Apparently, my program was listened to and had attracted an audience inside the prison because of my stance on human rights - a stance that was in keeping with that of Amnesty International – and because during the stand-off I was broadcasting nightly from a tent across the street from the prison, as were dozens of reporters from national and local media. Not being a journalist and therefore not restricted to the neutral position journalism required, I made sure my audience knew I was in complete sympathy with the prisoners' claims and understood what was happening to the people locked up inside. Reports prior to the uprising said the conditions at the Atlanta Pen were in violation of the rules governing treatment of federal prisoners, which became an ongoing subject of my program. The attorney said the inmates wanted to know if I would interview one of their spokesmen via telephone and broadcast the interview live. Of course, I would. In hindsight, I probably should have gotten permission from station management, but generally speaking, I've learned it's easier to get forgiveness than permission.

A cumbersome 1980s mobile phone was smuggled into the prison by one of the attorneys. It was assumed to be part of the equipment a sound technician carries, maybe something to do with recording a prisoner's statement, hidden in plain sight, so to speak. It looked like a case designed to carry a supply of batteries. Once inside, the attorney connected one of the uprising's leaders with my field producer and the interview began. The detainees' concern was their being held with no charges placed against them, an indefinite detention that would be repeated decades later at the U.S. military base at Guantanamo, Cuba, with captives from the other side of the globe. The irony of the second imprisonment is inescapable.

My questions and the Cuban's answers were short and to the point. There was no chatter about Cuba or Castro or U.S. policy concerning the island nation. The focus was the human rights of the people who had been imprisoned and how those rights were being violated by the U.S. government every day they continued to be held. It took no effort to hear the anguish in the words of the man who was talking with me. He also knew there was the possibility of being sent back to Cuba where yet another prison waited. The conversation ended abruptly when one of the U.S. Marshalls inside the prison realized a live interview was being conducted with – God forbid! – a "*journalist*" outside the prison, across the street where the scrum of reporters and camera operators had been camped for days waiting for the massive explosion and screams of pain that would announce what the cameras were waiting for, what they always wait for: violence on a massive scale. The smuggled phone was confiscated.

The television news business gives its undivided attention to blood and death and fires and explosions. If it bleeds, it leads the nightly newscast. In this instance, the media finally got a bit of what it came for. On November 23, mid-morning, the explosion came. The detainees took employees hostage, locking some of them in rooms next to the prison factory. Fire broke out. Firefighters were prevented from entering the prison grounds and a warehouse burned to the ground. The guards fled the scene, shooting and killing one of the Cubans as they bolted. The prisoners' frenzy increased. Eventually, 90 hostages were taken by the detainees. None was hurt. No one else died. And, then, after days of intense negotiations, the standoff ended, hostages were freed, and an agreement ending the deportations to Cuba was negotiated. The man almost solely responsible for a peaceful resolution to what could have been a horrific situation was Atlanta attorney Gary

Leshaw whose practice included civil rights litigation. Without his skill as both a negotiator and a human rights advocate, the Cuban prison uprising could have given the cameras exactly what they were waiting for: destruction and death. But, thanks to Leshaw that did not come.

It was shortly after the prison uprising and my on-site coverage that station management – from both programming and sales - called me in for what they said was to be a "program realignment" discussion. Yeah, that's what they called it. To me, it was corporate bullshit. Apparently, my interview and the pro-detainee phone calls it generated was a bit too "lefty" for WSB's tighty-whitey sales management whose department generated not only the station's profit, but also its image. One doesn't fuck with the sales department or the station's traditional on-air style. My audience obviously didn't agree. In fact, the Arbitron ratings system that every station subscribed to in order to determine the market's broadcast winners and losers – and thus the station's advertising rates – showed I was steadily increasing the number of listeners who tuned in to my program. Granted, I was in the most undesirable day part – five nights a week, 10PM to 1AM – but, because I was an honest-to-god liberal *(gasp!)* in a city that was looking for a more rational approach to solving political problems (because, you know, that would be good for business) than just adopting the usual repressive neo-Conservative stance, and the airwaves were saturated with that tiresome bullshit, and because the times *they were a'changin,'* my audience share kept increasing.

I sat through the meeting pretending to be interested in and focused on what the suits were saying. It required survival skills I didn't realize I had. These people owed their professional careers, and their existence, to a system that was not only unfair but also ultimately destructive. It was as though the rule was *"If You Can't Buy It, It Doesn't Exist"* and its corollary, *"If You Can't Make A Profit From It, It Has No Right To Exist."* I had begun to feel pity for their world-view. Pity and outrage. Of course, under a governing framework of capitalism, this rule and its corollary, permeated society. It was, in fact, the Most Important Thing - going all the way back to the enlightened white men who decided the structure of America. The documents they wrote that so eloquently laid out the reasons for revolution and how the new country would be constituted were just that: documents, sheets of parchment eventually to be placed in a museum. The reality was entirely different from the eloquence. Just ask the continent's native people and those people of color who were enslaved at the same time *"We hold these truths to be self-evident . . ."* was being written. Oh, wait. They're all dead.

But, I digress. The meeting with the station managers came quickly to the point: I was to ease up on all the social justice bullshit I was putting out nightly over their air. Be more mainstream, I was told. Realize that my ideas were a bit of a challenge to the station's long-time audience. But, I asked, wasn't that the point? To challenge those ideas? Uh, no. My reason for being there, they patiently explained, was to . . . entertain. I should have known that from the beginning. The suggestion was made that I should model my program, just a tad, in the direction of one of Atlanta's most adroit right-wingers. They were referring to one of my WSB stable-mates, the ridiculously conservative and intellectually deceptive Neal Boortz.

Neal claimed to be a Libertarian, which is in fact a right-winger who is trying to hide from the world's inconvenient truths, and who is willing to ignore Ayn Rand's blatantly hypocritical use of the social safety-net she so thoroughly denigrated in the twin bibles of the creepy Libertarian wanna-bes, "Atlas Shrugged" and its equally asinine companion screed, "The Fountainhead." All the abuse she heaped on New Deal and Great Society government programs such as Social Security and Medicare, was conveniently forgotten when she was ill and dying, and suddenly found that those programs were beneficial and necessary even to Libertarians like her. Surprise, surprise!

With few exceptions, Neal took the side of the neo-Fascist jerk-offs who even then were determined to undo and destroy all aspects of the beneficial social systems slowly put in place over the previous 60 years. Neal's attitude toward Social Security? Privatize it, turn it over to Wall Street. Medicare? Nothing but socialized medicine that would cause everyone to get sick and die a hideous death because only the sacrosanct market could determine the best care for desperately sick people. Medicaid? Communism, plain and simple. Neal also was vehemently opposed to any attempt by the federal government to keep in check, through reasonable regulation, the predatory capitalism that, left alone, guaranteed the U.S would forever be mired in inequality of opportunity, racism, income disparity on a criminal level, unequal jail sentencing guidelines, the wanton destruction of areas of natural beauty by the bastards who wanted to drill and mine and destroy, the denial of equal protection guaranteed by the Constitution, and on and on ad infinitum. In other words, Neal was contemptuous of just about anything designed to make life a bit easier, a little more interesting, sensual, and even possibly fun, *i.e.*, he was a right-wing lunatic.

For reasons obvious to both of us, including the fact we were polar opposites where it concerned anything political (and everything is political), or just Neal's inherent contempt for everyone not sharing his sour take on life, he and I did not share fun times or an occasional boys' night out. However, we did have occasion to go water skiing one summer afternoon, courtesy of WSB's management.

It was one of those corporate get-togethers so popular in the late 1980s. The idea being get everyone together, sales, production, technical, advertising, and management along with the fonts of energy that kept the whole thing going - the on-air talent - and from this mélange a hoped-for magic would occur that would elevate WSB to the realm of broadcast angels. Or, the real hope of management, a massive uptick in corporate profits. Or, some such bullshit. The massive pontoon party cruiser, trailing a 21-foot Chris Craft ski boat, was waiting at the dock when we all arrived by chartered bus at one of Lake Lanier's many marinas. After boarding and setting off into the lake's blue beauty, the booze began to flow. And flow. And, flow some more. Those few of us who were non-drinkers, clustered at the stern to surreptitiously share a joint of Oaxacan Gold. The party was on.

After several time-wasting speeches and presentations by the department managers, all of whom were male and all of whom were decked out in ridiculous looking boxy swim trunks, pastel-colored golf shirts, flip-flops and black dress socks, somebody suggested we go water-skiing. Absolutely! I ducked into one of the cabins and changed into my black Speedos. I had been wearing Speedos, or its equivalent, since my early teen years when I swam competitively for Glass City Aquatic

183

Club in Toledo, Ohio. They were tight, form-hugging, nylon that offered the least resistance in the water, true engineering marvels in the 50s. Apparently, I was the only male on the boat who had ever swum in competition. Either that or everyone else enjoyed wearing floppy, baggy, trunks that came down to the knees and made their legs look like hairy spindles.

Back on deck, I fastened the ski belt around my waist, grabbed the handle of the tow rope, and jumped into the water. The boat was driven by one of the sales geeks who was half in the bag from several Jack Blacks and no lunch, but, not to worry; I was an accomplished swimmer and had a flotation belt snug around my mid-section. Sales geek did an excellent job, smashed or not. Long straight-a-ways down open water in the massive lake, lazy turns, a few pin-wheels for excitement, a couple of spills, and, after several high-velocity passes around the party boat, back to the pontoon and the crowd of now totally sloshed, stoned and FUBARed employees of the Voice of the South. Except for Neal. Neal was sober as a judge. As I climbed up the pontoon's ladder and back on deck, Neal, who had been eyeing my mid-section as I struggled to get back aboard, let loose with, "Hey! It's Speedo Malloy! How was the ride, Speedo? Didja' get wet? Haw-haw-haw! Speedo! Hurt anything when you went ass-over-elbows out there?"

All his cackling and yelling about my goddam Speedos got the attention of every female on board. Neal was giving them a guided tour of my crotch, which was perfectly okay with me, although the upper management guys, the ones making mental notes of the festivities – which employees were obnoxiously drunk, who was going back to the stern repeatedly and why, in addition to making note of who was passed out on the deck chairs - were frowning and mumbling to each other each time Neal let loose with another "Speeeeee-do!" Apparently, making visible the contours and outlines of one's groin under a wet Speedo was not acceptable corporate behavior. Especially when an obnoxious asshole like Neal kept shrieking, *"Speeee-do, Speeee-do!"* All in all, the boat ride was a typical example of corporate "fun." An attempt to let us "associates" know that management really, really cared.

Over the next few days there were several lunch invitations from girls in the sales department left on my studio answering machine, thanks to Neal's attention-focusing squeals of *"Speeeee-do . . .!"* and for that maybe I should thank him. The pontoon meeting itself? Didn't learn shit.

Chapter 16

Pansy Truck

My audience numbers continued to go up. The subjects I focused on were topics guaranteed to cause serious heartburn in WSB's executive suite. Gay issues – which was a topic management wished would just go away, even though the AIDS epidemic was slicing through the nation's creative population, including Atlanta's, like the Four Horsemen of the Apocalypse let loose – was a subject critical to Atlanta's large and now traumatized homosexual community, especially when the Commissioners of Cobb County, one of Atlanta's suburban counties, decided to pass a resolution condemning what they insisted on calling the "gay life-style," and then, as an additional slap in the face, if you somehow missed the point of their Christian bigotry, decided to cut off all county arts funding rather than having to make decisions regarding what would and would not offend the delicate sensibilities of their citizens. God forbid some radical queer would produce art that, through some subtle shutter click or brush stroke or spoken word, would bring about the downfall of Christian civilization, starting in Cobb County, Georgia.

Adding insult to grievous injury, this was the county where the sick fuck J.B. Stoner - who eventually was convicted of being one of the perpetrators of the 1958 bombing of the 16th Street Baptist Church in Birmingham, Alabama, and the resulting deaths of four young Black girls who were attending Sunday School - lived and organized his national hate campaigns against anyone who wasn't a white, male, Klan-sympathizing, Christian, right-wing lunatic. Like him.

After two years of displaying their stupidity for the world to see, the county resolution was rescinded after the daughter of the County Commission Chairman – a man who was a devout church-going hypocrite - came out as a lesbian which was not just ironic, it was a richly deserved smack-down to the Christian bigots who had tried to make life miserable for yet another community of people who did not meet the bigots' Caucasian, hetero-maniacal definition of how proper and acceptable people comported themselves and with whom it was proper to have sex. Uh, *married* sex.

Human rights was an issue I felt compelled to discuss as a recurring theme on my program. I, like so many who lived through the 1980s, saw a grim and soul-devouring succession of young, creative men destroyed by the AIDS virus – not a few of them my friends. Attending funerals became a frequent sad event and the sadness was never mitigated no matter how many memorial services; the anguish only became more deeply embedded, which may explain the anger I felt driving in to work one night.

I was listening to the program host who was on right before me when he cut away to commercials. This was usually when I'd flip to another station to avoid hearing the same ads I'd be listening to, over and over, for the next three hours. But, before I could change stations I heard the beginning of an ad that turned out to be a Mazda truck commercial. It was quickly obvious the commercial had been designed and produced for the Southern market. A couple of redneck-sounding males were talkin' 'bout whut kinda' truck they really liked.

Redneck One: "I work at a big ol' pulp-wood mill and I need a heavy-duty truck, one that'll work as hard as I do!"

Redneck Two: "I hear ya'! Me? I spend my days at the gravel pit, bustin' that granite into pieces small enough so as not to tear up the tires on the cars that drive these country roads. Now, that's some hard labor, pal!"

Redneck One: "And, the last thing we want or need is some *pansy* truck when we get off work, right?"

Redneck Two: "Boy, you got that right! Don't need no *pansy* truck! Gotta have a tough, he-man Mazda truck!"

What the fuck?! A *pansy* truck? What, pray tell, would a *pansy* truck be? One that wore a blond wig and dressed like a (gasp!) bitch? Like that? Is that a *pansy* truck? Well, I had my first topic for the show that night. A *pansy* truck . . .?!

Before going to the broadcast booth, I went to the Program Director's office and told him what I wanted to do. The whole pansy truck commercial was too much. Everyone knew what the word "pansy" referred to and it had nothing to do with a colorful little flower.

"Greg," I said, sitting down without being invited to, "that is one fucked up commercial, and whether they meant to or not, whoever created it has a dog whistle in there that is almost ear-shattering. I have to take the ad agency who put that together to the mat. I mean, what fucking genius in New York or wherever thought they were connecting to dumb-shit Southern men who would really clue in on not wanting 'no pansy truck?' "

"Yeah, I heard that, too," he answered. "Weird way to sell trucks. You think anyone will notice the pansy part?"

"Notice? *Notice?* I wouldn't be surprised if several thousand protesters showed up tomorrow morning with signs saying 'WSB is anti-gay,' or 'WSB' means We're Such Bigots. Jesus, Greg, we just got over the Cobb County bullshit."

"What do you want to do?"

"Just point out the stupidity in producing that sort of commercial, where they think their target market in the South is nothing but anti-gay, male rednecks, which, okay, a lot of them are, but, Jesus, Greg, not all of them, right?" He said go ahead. As it turned out, that okay was a big error. For me.

Now, to take on a marketing company, to challenge the stupidity so often found in commercials (and especially an agency that spends lots of money to advertise on your radio station) as I did that night carries with it the chance someone is going to become very, very upset, someone in a position of power in that agency who might be inclined to retaliate by cancelling accounts, which means a loss of revenue for the station, which means, station management will, in turn, get very, very upset, which means being called into the station manager's office where the person who sold the ad will scream, *"What the fuck were you thinking? Do you realize how much money your little pro-gay shit last night cost me?"* because the ad agency just cancelled a contract that meant the loss of hundreds of thousands of ad dollars and the evaporation of huge commissions for the sales geek who had worked on getting the agency as a client for months and had – on her own -approved the copy for this ad, which means the Program Director who, by the way, had been with the station for only

189

three months, would suffer the fury of station management for allowing such a deconstructing of an ad that simply denigrated thousands of people who happen to be gay, and the station is in the business to make money and not get all misty-eyed for gay folk who are harassed, taunted, beaten, and even killed here in the Buckle of the Bible Belt, that's someone else's job, so now how do we handle this short of firing not just the manager, who was stupid enough to okay this little venture in social engineering, but also the liberal freak who went on the air and came to the defense of people who are gay, fuck their struggle with AIDS!!! And, all of it, management implied, caused by my calling out an ad about a goddam pick-up truck, okay a pansy truck when, in fact, a huge percentage of WSB's listeners saw it as a perfectly legitimate reference for these pushy queers with their gay rights and pride parades and demands they be treated like normal people while God is obviously punishing the whole lot of them with AIDS!!!!

Or something very close to that.

So, I listened to the reprimand while I wondered why the fuck I was working at a radio station that was proud of their anti-everything that wasn't white, conservative, and passive in the face of ongoing bullshit heaped on minority folk. A severe character flaw? It was time for a break, a real one, one that would separate me from the crazed reality stream I had gotten sucked into. Enter peyote.

Chapter 17

In The Woods

I had five roommates. We shared an antebellum, run-down mansion that soon would be demolished to make way for modern, upscale condos needed for the heavy influx of Yuppies and Buppies who were swarming into Atlanta. But, for now, it was ours, ghosts and all. Three levels, a terraced back yard, massive oaks and tall pine trees that, when the wind blew, whispered the horrors the ancient trees had heard when the house belonged to a slave owner.

We were two actors, a writer, a photographer, and a woman studying at Georgia State to be an urban planner. That was our core population. In addition, at any given time, there would be another roomie or two, usually an Emory University student or a would-be painter lost in the attic, maybe a blues musician searching for a gig. A fun group. Every Sunday morning we'd all gather on the rear sun porch for a thrown-together brunch; bagels, fruit, smoked salmon, maybe a potato knish, mixed with Darvon, aspirin, and whatever else was the latest cure for severe hangovers brought on by both alcohol and 'Ludes.

On one of these Sunday get-togethers the photographer –

call him Rick – asked if any of us wanted to ingest a few peyote buds. A friend of his had recently returned from the Sonoran Desert with a supply of the little rascals. I said *me, me! Pick me!* I had never tried peyote but had heard it was a consciousness raising experience not to be missed. Of course, I heard that from a woman who made a very good living selling all sorts of mind-expanding potions and plants, as well as ancient bits and shards of pottery and fossilized cooking utensils she had collected during her travels in the Middle East. Even though I believed her and thought she was a very interesting traveler, I never opened myself to the power of peyote. But, I was curious. I had read both *The Teachings of Don Juan (A Yaqui Way of Knowledge),* and *A Separate Reality ,* so when Rick made his offer, I saw my chance to go all Carlos Castenada and maybe find my spirit ally. If I had one.

We decided the following Saturday would be the day to make our journey to the great beyond, given our erratic schedules. I asked my friend, Katy, who passed on participating in the actual experience, to go along as sort of an anchor in this reality in case I needed rescuing. Katy, bless her heart, agreed. "I'll just smoke a joint while you guys find your doors of perception," she said, wickedly. Rick asked one of our roommates, Sara, who was studying taxidermy if she wanted the experience. She said yes, because that might put her in contact with the spirits of the feathery little animal carcasses she would slice open in order to do her taxidermy studies, studies which included placing little bird corpses in our shared house refrigerator which could really freak you out at three o'clock in the morning when you stumbled half-awake to the fridge to get a glass of cold water and there the little boogers were, all stiff and dead and sad looking. Sara was extremely strange.

And, that was our little group, three of us going off to find the wizard if the wizard dwelt inside a peyote button, and a fourth to get help if we needed rescuing.

Saturday arrived. We all got together in the kitchen to watch Rick make the necessary preparations. He brought in a paper bag, opened it, and pulled out several handfuls of gruesome-looking chunks of cactus tops. As soon as he opened the bag a very weird smell filled the kitchen and I immediately felt like running away. Far away. This was some dangerous shit for an unstable person to encounter. The smell said it all. Into a pot of boiling spring water went the peyote buds. We waited. After 30 minutes or so Rick removed the buds, all swollen and fleshy now, and poured the yellowish water into a thermos bottle. The buds (they appeared to be twitching slightly) went back into the bag where I'm sure they felt uncomfortable.

We piled into Katy's car and headed north out of Atlanta. Forty miles away on the banks of the Etowah River, deep into an old-growth forest, Katy's family had built a cabin in the shape of a geodesic dome. Her father was a well-known psychotherapist and this setting was the one he used for his more agitated patients, the theory being the forest and the gently flowing river and the peacefulness, taken together, were calming and conducive to reflection and the examination of one's inner self.

Eventually, Katy turned off the two-lane highway onto a gravel road that soon gave way to a dusty, reddish clay track, that, in turn, disappeared altogether as we got deeper into the woods, until she was driving on a faintly visible, pine needle covered trail that led to the dome. There it sat, perfectly blended into the surrounding forest, unpainted, rustic and peaceful. We got out of the car and went inside. The immediate effect was calming, indeed. The walls and ceiling were large, clear triangles of clear glass; the wood floors and interior stairs that rose to a loft were sweet-smelling cedar, and in the middle of the circular inner space was a stone fireplace surrounded by built-in padded couches. Nestled under the stairway was a small kitchen with a four-burner gas stove next to a metal sink. Cedar cabinets were built into the space above the sink. Outside, a deck attached to the dome seemed independently suspended and part of the forest. It had been built to allow the trees to remain rising through holes in the deck floor. After wandering around for a few minutes taking in the beauty of the place, we gathered on the couches for our peyote tutorial. Rick, having made the trip before, was the tutor.

"You may experience what seem to be hallucinations," he began. "However, that's not what they are. What you see and hear will be as real as the conversation we are having now. This new reality can be very intense, both in terms of learning and disorientation. However, there is no reason to fear what you will find yourself part of." Rick had entered lecture mode. He was sounding like a professor of anthropology. "There are no monsters," he continued, "nothing to be afraid of, nothing that will make you lose your mind unless you want to let it go. And this is important: one of the benefits and healing powers of peyote is you *can* lose your mind, your old mind, the one corrupted with lies and deceit and bigotry and fear, all that nasty input collected over years of self-deception." I had that feeling again, the one that said *run!* when Rick was boiling the buds back at the house, which, right now, seemed to be somewhere on another planet, far away and long ago.

"Only you will determine the depth of your experience and

how much you will learn from it. Just don't panic at any time. You are safe in the arms of peyote."

"What? 'The arms of peyote'? Isn't that just a tad dramatic, Professor Rick, a bit over the top there?"

"Just trying to set a comfortable mood, man. It's all good." I had lived with Rick for two years and knew he could go all mysterious when he felt it would enhance his photography. I felt just a bit foolish for questioning his choice of words. After all, this was a tutorial. Maybe there were "arms of peyote." What the fuck did I know? Nothing.

"Katy will be close by if you need assistance in sorting things out, both during and after," he said, resting his hand on Katy's arm. "Any questions?"

I raised my hand, a thoroughly ridiculous move given there were only two of us who might have a question. "Will I die?" Rick smiled and rolled his eyes.

Rick went to the kitchen and came back with three small drinking glasses, partially filled with the water in which the buds had been boiled. "Let's drink this first. It will get us started. I added some mint to offset the taste. Then we'll chew the buttons and swallow them."

The mint didn't help very much. The taste was what fetid swamp water smelled like, nasty, brutish and thick. On Rick's instruction we tilted our heads back and emptied the glasses. Then, the buttons, limp now, green and yellow, and very fibrous. It was difficult to chew, even harder to swallow. I managed to get four of them down and almost immediately felt a rush of violent nausea and gut pain accompanied by a rippling stomach convulsion, as though the peyote was trying to climb back out of my body, to escape. Before we left the house, after Rick had boiled the peyote buds, we each took a paring knife and carefully removed the little white pustules of strychnine that lived on top of the cactus. We missed a few, that was now clear.

We walked outside. I noticed a new sensation as a breeze stirred against my bare arms. I could see the ripples in the air as it undulated around the dome, around Katy, around Rick and Sara as they walked off into the woods becoming smaller and smaller until they disappeared. There was a faint melody being played somewhere, soft with sharp edges, a sound unfamiliar. A lute? An aulos? It didn't matter. Identities were fluid now.

I made my way to what appeared to be a pile of small, sun-splashed boulders sitting near a stand of tall oaks. Katy walked off toward the river, climbed part way up a sugar maple, and settled back to watch the rippling flow of the Etowah. Then she morphed into a hawk and flew away, her raptor's screech echoing through the forest. I settled down into the stone curves and depressions in the boulders. They scooted around a bit to make me comfortable, all the while sighing as though my presence was mildly disturbing. To my left, one of the larger ones opened a deep cleft in its middle and a clear stream of icy water flowed into an earthen cup I hadn't noticed when I sat. The sun felt warm and I could see the brilliant particles that made up the individual beams streaming down through the trees like tiny pieces of copper foil. I wondered when Katy had learned how to fly and if she did it often. A sudden wind appeared and danced in front of me. It gathered force, pushing pine cones and acorns and debris from the forest floor around me toward the river. I was able to see each vein of each leaf as it all tumbled past in a mad rush to the water. The branches of the trees, even the smaller ones, were not moving in this wind. The rush of air was having no effect on the trees at all.

I wondered how that could be. The wind always agitates tree leaves, doesn't it? Isn't there some law of physics about that? Inertia? Brisk wind equals moving leaves hanging from the trees. That's the way it always works. There was no sound, except for a deep, low, almost imperceptible vibration that felt like it was coming from the boulders that had now pushed up around me. I lifted the cup of cold water and drank. Just beyond my peripheral vision I sensed slight movement above and to my left, away from the now placid, silent river. Small, inverted pyramids of energy (I guessed) were settling down, down onto and into the trees, whose greens and browns and blacks were made deeper shades of color. The trees were glowing, a halo of light filling the spaces among them until there was no empty space left, just fluid, warm light. It was one of the larger oaks, if not the largest, that spoke first.

"Arrogance will destroy you." The forest floor vibrated slightly from the deep bass voice that was not angry with its question, just curious.

"Am I arrogant?" I asked, not the least freaked that a tree had just spoken to me.

"Yes. All of you are, you twitching, jerking creatures." The voice continued with a litany of questions. "Why do you move around? Can you not find a place of balance and stay there? Why do you kill us? Why do you slice us into pieces? Why do you burn us into charred stumps?"

"I don't do that. I've never done that. I wouldn't do that." I had to offer a convincing denial. I sensed that if I didn't, something unpleasant would happen. I could feel a sudden cascade of anxiety flow around me, washing away my initial feelings of wonder and warmth, as if an outer covering was being peeled off me.

The tree spoke again. "Do you understand the danger of arrogance?"

"No, I really don't. I mean, I guess so. It's not good, right? Have I offended you?" I didn't wait for an answer. "Listen, my best friend when I was a kid playing in my grandma's orchard was a tree, an apple tree. Its branches were my horse, my sailing ship, my castle. Every summer. My imagination was limitless then."

"You didn't offend me. Not you personally. Do you remember the yellow cat?"

The yellow cat . . .

Suddenly, "Yes! I do!"

I hadn't thought of the yellow cat for decades. The first time I saw it was a in bright flash at the far edge of the orchard. I had been sailing the oceans, stopping at deserted islands, foraging into the jungles to find something to eat. After walking for a few minutes and not finding anything I thought was edible, I stopped at the edge of a chasm that cut through the undergrowth. It was deep and strewn with volcanic boulders at the bottom. On the other side, about 25 meters away, I saw the yellow cat, smiling at me. It was a big house cat, huge in fact, and its tail dangled over the edge of the chasm.

"Come to this side," the yellow cat whispered. "There are things you must know. I can tell you what they are. Come across."

"But, I can't," I said, tears all at once filling my eyes and starting to flow down my cheeks. "I want to, but I can't. I might fall into this chasm and there's no one to help me get back out if I do. I'm sorry. I'm so sorry." I was crying freely now, my tears becoming a stream that rushed from my face and flowed into the valley that separated us. "I want to, but I can't. Do you understand that?"

"There is no valley," it answered. "Just come down from that tree and walk over here. You've done that every day; climb up, climb down. Just walk over here."

I couldn't. I was too afraid. The cat was too big to be real. Then, it smiled. I knew cats couldn't smile. I stopped crying.

"This is the only time you'll see me," it continued. "After this moment, I will fade from your memory and your dreams. So, this, then, is why I am here, why you see me now . . ."

And, after a while, it stopped talking. The orchard began to slip out of focus. "Wait! What are the things? What do I have to know?" The cat disappeared, leaving a yellow halo where it had been sitting.

"So, you do remember," the Voice said.

"Yes, but so what? That was just a stupid kid thing when I was ten years old. Maybe even a dream. It was nothing."

"Really? Nothing?"

The thick undergrowth nearby began moving, being pushed aside. I felt a sudden fear that I couldn't contain. I had to run. I had to get away from whatever was moving through the dense kudzu and twisted blackberry bushes. I pushed against the rocks, lifting myself up, and ran towards the river. Katy had promised she'd be there if I needed help. But, Katy had flown away. I turned around and saw a figure, a person, walking toward me. It was a man wrapped in a blanket, with a rope belt tied around his waist and a hood over his head.

"Here! I have something for you," he shouted, his hand outstretched. He stopped walking. "It's yours. I believe you lost it."

I could hear the river behind me, now. It was churning and

foaming, the tops of tumbling whitecaps stinging against the back of my neck.

"Who are you?" I shouted in return. "I haven't lost anything. What's in your hand?"

The river was moaning, surging against its banks.

"It's yours, he said. "You don't remember losing it? It was a long time ago, but surely you remember. Here."

"Honestly, I don't want whatever you're holding. I don't know what you're holding. Throw it away."

"Throw it away? That's funny. That's really funny. How can I throw away something that's not mine?"

"That's crazy," I answered. "Just open your hand and let this wind take it. I don't want it, whatever it is. Do you understand me?"

The man continued walking toward me. I couldn't move. I wanted to run again. I couldn't.

"Don't be so difficult," he said, still moving toward me. "You need to have this. It's important."

As he talked I had a sense of being tugged, pulled, even though I was still unable to move at all. I could feel a force pulling this way, then pushing that way, then pulling again. I was being pulled apart. I felt a space opening up between me here and me there. It wasn't painful. It felt like two different people hugging me, drawing me into an embrace. And, then there were two of me. Crazy. When I lifted my hand, so did I lift my hand. When I nodded my head, so did I nod my head.

"What is happening? What is this? I don't like this," I and I said.

"See?" the man laughed. "You need the protection. You can't be you and you. You can only be one."

I and I held out my hand. This had to stop. He stepped closer and placed a folded piece of paper in my and my hand. It was old and smelled like a wood fire, and sweat, and something else, something I and I couldn't name. Grease? Animal grease from a wood fire?

I closed my eyes and opened them, and I was one again. Just me. Not me and me. Off to my left, the yellow cat appeared. "Hey, wait a minute!" I shouted. "You just said I'd never see you again! So, what's this? I see you again. You said I wouldn't even remember you. What? Five minutes ago?"

The yellow cat laughed. Laughed. "That was a long time ago when I said that. Years. In the orchard."

This fucking yellow cat was about to make me crazy. "The orchard," I shouted, "was when I was a kid. That was, what? Thirty-five years ago? You don't make any sense at all. What is your deal, cat? I mean, really. This is nuts."

"The piece of paper, do you still have it?" the yellow cat was licking a paw and wiping its cheek.

"After thirty-five years??!"

It was in the right rear pocket of my jeans. I took it out and once again the smell of burning wood floated around me. The paper was folded over several times, deeply creased, and stained with deep brown splotches. I unfolded it slowly, so I wouldn't tear it or further shred its damp edges.

The yellow cat spoke: "Hold on a minute. Don't open it just yet. Let's talk about this."

I stopped trying to open the piece of paper. "Talk? About what?"

"What's written down on that paper. What it says."

It was trying to slide it back into my hip pocket. "You mean talk about how crazy all this is, right? This . . . what is this? This place and you and all this stuff that's happening."

"Do you want to go back to where you were," the cat winked at me.

"And, where would that be? Right now, I don't know where I am and therefore couldn't tell you where I would go back to? How's that, cat?"

"You're a hard one. This is not difficult to figure out. It's yours to begin with so I don't get what the problem is here, I really don't."

"Just let me get back to the rocks I was sitting in, under that huge oak. That'll be good. Just right back there." And, I was there, under the tree, in the rocks.

"So, where did you go? Did you meet anyone interesting?" the huge oak tree asked. Yeah, that's how it had to happen. Yellow cat and the man in the blanket and the note – mustn't forget the note – just disappeared, gone, not even a squeaky hinge as the door shut behind them. The rocks were still comfy.

"Where'd I go? That's funny. Where did I go? Well, Mighty Oak, nowhere, I guess. Just stayed here. Lotta shit happened, though. By the way, can you tell the time by looking at the sun or the length of the shadows? I'm trying to guess what time it is and I'm sure you're not wearing a watch."

In the distance, far away, bouncing among the hills, tumbling from branch to branch among the tallest pines, the *skreeeeeeeee* . . . of a hawk. A red-tailed hawk.

"Aren't you going to look at the note? The folded paper?"

"Okay, sure. You are insistent for a tree."

I unfolded the paper, slowly, carefully, as it was old and brittle. The smell of a wood fire flooded around me as I opened it. I stared at it, not believing what it was. A crude map with what appeared to be random lines leading to a dark X. I could still read what was written under the X: *where he will be waiting.*

For no reason I could think of, I started trembling.

My back hurt from leaning against the rough texture of the rocks, my right leg a buzzing phantom. The sunlight was being absorbed by the forest's shadows. I looked up at the tree near the river bank just as the hawk landed on an upper branch, its wings fluttering until it was balanced. Katy was climbing down the tree, smiling, and looking into me more deeply than anyone ever had. I could feel her moving around inside me.

"So . . ., " she said, as she walked over and gave me a hug. "You okay? Did you have fun?"

"Yeah, I think. Maybe not fun in the usual sense, though. More like weird fun, you know, where you're not really sure it's fun. Like the first time you see circus clowns and you're pretty sure you should be laughing like the adults are but what you really feel like doing is screaming as loud as you can and running away as fast as you can, right? Weird."

"Well, I had the most wonderful flying dreams while you all were exploring all your little nooks and crannies. It was so nice sitting in that tree, stoned and relaxed, feeling the breeze, and then just drifting off to sleep. Perfect."

"Are the others back, yet?"

They were. Even as I asked the question, Rick and Sara came walking out of the shadows and into the dimming circle of sunlight where Katy and I stood waiting.

"So . . .?" I wanted to hear their story. "What happened?" Both burst out laughing. "We . . . uh . . . met some people . . ." More laughing.

"That funny, huh?" I said, feeling left out of the fun.

Sara: "I wouldn't know where to start. It wasn't funny, that was a nervous, thank-god-we're-back laugh. No, not funny . . ."

203

Rick: "You know about golems, right?"

Me: "Sure. Something you Jews came up with. A little monster, made of mud and dust, stuff like that, lifeless. Like banshees and *jinis*. Same kind of crazy shit, different religions."

Rick: "Yeah, well, we walked into a whole goddam village of them."

Sara: "They started jumping around, trying to touch us. Reaching out with those long fingers . . ." she shuddered.

Rick: "We finally got that they wanted us to follow them, away from their caves and into the forest. Uh-huh, no thanks!"

Sara: "So, we took off the other way. What we saw . . . Rick? You try. I still can't find the words . . . but, it was beautiful."

Rick: "The first thing I did was reach into my back-pack for my camera. Not there. I guess it's in the cabin. The colors, though. That's what was so spectacular."

Sara: "More than that. More than spectacular."

Rick: "You remember that long bit in Space Odyssey where what's-his-name is ripping through time and those incredible colors and shapes were blowing by him? Like that."

Me: "Keir Dullea. Wish I would've been wherever the hell you two were . . . I was busy talking with a cat and a tree and some weird dude in a blanket."

Beyond those snap-shot descriptions, there wasn't much more to tell each other that would have made objective sense. It was all about perception and consciousness and interior landscape and being flooded with everything that is so, moment to moment, effectively blocked. A doorway, an entrance, a path that leads as far into awareness as one can tolerate, which, when you consider our lost ability to "see", isn't very far at all.

Chapter 18

The March

January, 1987.

The idea of a massive civil rights march came after a few dozen beer-drinking, rebel flag waving whites a week earlier had thrown stones and bottles and screamed "nigger" at a small collection of activists who had organized a ''walk for brotherhood'' from the northern suburbs of Atlanta to the Forsyth County courthouse. The march was designed to focus attention on the all-white county's long and violent history of racism and the continuing refusal to accept black people moving into the area. The marchers were tired of being burned by the dying embers of Jim Crow and, by marching, decided to let the white, Christian citizens of Forsyth County understand that their darker brothers and sisters were simply acting on all the civil rights legislation that had been passed into law during the past quarter century. In other words, just trying to be law-abiding citizens of the United States.

Of course, the whites didn't see it that way at all. These Atlanta trouble-makers were breaking the law, not upholding it, which meant the small number of activists who marched along a paved road that wound through the countryside, starting from a boarded-up strip mall and ending at the county courthouse in Cumming, Georgia, a distance of less than five miles, were seen as a threat to the county's peace and tranquility that far from being peaceful and tranquil, was what one could expect in semi-rural Georgia: The caustic effects of religious quackery, domestic violence, alcoholism and drug addiction; county cops who used whatever terror tactics got the results they were seeking when they made an arrest, child abuse, gun deaths, hatred of blacks, and racist contempt for seasonal farm workers from Mexico and Central America.

To the county residents, however, violence and drug addiction and religious insanity were not the cause of their problems. Rather, it was an ever-lengthening list of societal changes forced on them from the outside world that was eating holes in the order of things, order that had been established more than a century ago and backed by laws written to maintain the political and social and enforcement power of the whites, no matter the violence, no matter the nuttery, no matter the addiction, no matter what.

The whites refused to recognize the changes that were being delivered to their county thanks to unstoppable urban sprawl. Those changes were immutable. Atlanta, a not so long-ago day's ride away by wagon or mule, was expanding at an exponential rate, devouring what once was farm land, woods, hills and streams, and turning it all into shopping centers, subdivisions, office parks, schools, mega-churches, manufacturing plants, and, finally, the final insult, a six-lane divided highway slicing through Forsyth County, the *sine qua non* of the expanding Atlanta exurbs.

The whites tried to say "no" to the approaching changes

206

they had no realistic hope of stopping, especially where it concerned the new realities of race relations, the only way they knew how: Their own angry demonstrations, complete with Cross of St. Andrew flags, white, pointy-headed Klan costumes, army fatigues, beer, muscle shirts, motorcycles, baseball bats, shouts of "Nigger" and, for the whites marching for justice, "Nigger-lover."

The small group of participants in the first march – forced to turn back towards Atlanta under a barrage of rocks, bottles, clubs and death threats - had no idea their small demonstration would lead to the largest civil rights action since "Bloody Sunday" at the Pettus bridge in Selma, Alabama, in 1965. However, the actions taken by the Forsyth County locals in response to this peaceful attempt to push through yet another racial barrier led to this winter march that brought thousands to the small Georgia town of Cumming, Forsyth's county seat.

The area was settled by Cherokee First Nations people beginning in the mid-1700s. Even early in its history, the area was the site of bloody violence. After two years of a war of attrition caused by disputes over hunting land, the Cherokee defeated their rivals, the Creek nation, and forced them south, away from the lush mountain territory. For the next 75 years the Cherokee coexisted with the white settlers who were inexorably moving onto land the native people considered to be theirs, given to them by the Great Spirit. The peace, such as it was, ended with the 1828 discovery of gold in north Georgia. Five years later the city of Cumming was formed and within two years a treaty with whites was signed that said the Cherokee must leave. This "Treaty of New Echota" led to a forced migration that resulted in the deaths of thousands along what came to define yet another in the endless horrors perpetrated by immigrant whites against native people, the "Trail of Tears." Employing terror tactics, including the utter destruction of native villages, the whites forced the Cherokee to march from Georgia to the "Indian Territory" west of the Mississippi River, to settle on land completely foreign to the mountain-dwelling natives. At the same time, the California gold rush in 1849 put an end to any interest in mining in Cumming and the small city sank into an economic depression that turned modest prosperity into desperate poverty. Newly built railroads that were spreading across the South from the Atlanta transportation hub bypassed Cumming altogether. Because of its new isolation, the city devolved into one more bleak, poverty-drenched Southern mountain town, cut off from commerce and any further development. Ironically, it was this isolation that spared the city when General William T. Sherman made his infamous "march to the sea" near the end of the Civil War. Just 40 miles south Sherman laid waste to Atlanta by burning it to the ground.

A half-century later, racial violence of a different kind erupted in Cumming. In 1912, Georgia Governor Joseph Brown ordered the state militia to Cumming to prevent anarchy after several reported rapes of white women allegedly by black men. One of those men, named Rob Edwards, was dragged from the Cumming city jail where he was being held for the rape of a white woman. He was shot and wounded by Klansmen, and then hanged from an electric power pole on the town square. Worried the terror would spread, the governor declared martial law, but, according to reports published at the time, the effort did little to stop a month-long barrage of Klan-led attacks against black citizens across the county. This rampage of murderous violence finally led to the virtual banishment of all black residents. The county became a whites-only enclave with no black population at all.

It soon became apparent that the second civil rights march into Forsyth County, after the small group of civil rights advocates was stoned and chased away a few weeks earlier, was going to be yet another milestone in the long struggle for equal protection – as well as equal rights - under the law. Word of the planned demonstration was spreading across the country. National as well as local news organizations were descending on the county and were not disappointed in looking for obvious signs of racial discrimination flourishing half-an-hour north of the much-touted capital of The New South. The locals were all too willing to offer clownish caricatures of white supremacy still flourishing in pockets of the old Confederacy. Kluxers and their sympathizers – neo-Nazis, white supremacists, Christian Identity crazies – were coming from Alabama, South Carolina, and, of course, Mississippi to add their presence to the growing army of white morons who, with their Confederate battle flags held aloft seemed intent on convincing the congealing press that they were as ignorant as they were loud. Regalia-draped Klansmen and their sheeted wives and girlfriends paraded around in circles for hours, shouting "nigger!" and "go back to New York!" at anyone they didn't recognize, including other white people from nearby North Georgia communities. And, while the clown shows in Cumming continued daily, a real army of National Guardsmen and law-enforcement officers were being given orders to deploy to Forsyth County, Georgia.

The morning of the march, January 25th, arrived chilly, misty, and tense with the expectation of potential conflict. In what Georgia's then-governor described as "the greatest

209

show of force the state has ever marshalled," military, state troopers from three states, and local law enforcement officers had bivouacked in the parking lot of an abandoned strip mall three miles south of the county courthouse. Their mission was to maintain order, which meant ignore the vile language and threats from the assembled locals while keeping the racist types separate from the civil rights marchers, and immediately arrest those who showed the slightest refusal to obey the commands of the police.

Slowly, the number of marchers increased. The number of counter-demonstrators also increased which led to more racist taunts, more shouts of "fuck you, nigger-lovers!" from the hooded Klan types and their strange family members: kids with rotting teeth, grannies who appeared to be strung out from too much meth, big-haired bottle-blonde wives , good ol' boys with their bloated beer bellies bulging over the tops of their faux army fatigues, and all gathered along this two-lane black-top to curse and scream violent threats at the thousands of people who ignored their endlessly repeated bullshit and slowly began forming up for the march toward the county courthouse.

The march staging area was flooded with the noise made by the huge crowd. The roaring diesel engines of the National Guard troop carriers filled the air with eye-stinging fumes. Above, the staccato drone of police helicopters gave the feeling of being in a combat medical-evacuation zone. The shouted orders from military non-coms could be heard above the ever-increasing din of thousands of voices. By the hundreds, the Guardsmen formed parallel lines of troops on either side of the road, a clear warning to the yelling, jeering counter-demonstrators that even the hint of violence directed towards the marchers would not be tolerated and would be met with military force.

Pre-selected parade marshals began directing the growing mass of marchers towards the two-lane blacktop that led to the heart of Cumming. Slowly, the huge crowd began to form up into a moving mass of multi-hued humanity. Then, a long pause while the marchers waited for the arrival of Coretta Scott King, Dr. Martin Luther King's widow, whose chartered bus had just pulled into the mall parking lot after the short ride from Atlanta. A march of this scope, this size, with this objective, could only be led by a person with the stature of Mrs. King. Shoulder to shoulder with her husband, she had taken part in so many actions against racism and poverty, hunger and discrimination; today would be yet another in an endless succession of protests against the cruelty of institutionalized racism. With her arrival, the march began.

I was carrying the latest in audio recording technology, thanks to one of the engineers at WSB. My plan for the day was simple. I would march with the demonstrators and, along the way, interview not only a few of the marchers, but also one or two of the screaming whites lining the country road: the white power types, the Klan goofs, the Rebel re-loads with their anachronistic Confederate battle flags. I had taken a position about a third of the way back from the leaders of the march, along with Angela, one of the obviously nervous women from the station's news department who was there as a credentialed reporter for WSB. "Stay close, please," she said, as we stepped off with the rest of the now clapping, singing, chanting crowd. I could barely hear her even though only inches separated us. "Crowds like this make me nervous," she added. "I'm afraid there might be a stampede and I'll get trampled." The mist and fog had disappeared in the warm morning sunlight and the heat from the crowd had removed the early chill. As we walked, Angela jotted down in her reporter's note-pad bits of conversation from the people around us. "Are you going to do a feature piece on all this?" I asked.

"Yeah, that's my assignment this weekend. Of course, I was coming to this march anyway. I was too young to take part in any of the civil rights stuff in the 60s and 70s. I read about it, though. So, when I heard about this march I knew I had to be here. I called my mom and told her, and she said be careful, you're in Georgia! My news director said, 'Well, if you're gonna be there anyway, might as well give us a report.'"

"Are you getting paid?"

She smiled, "Actually, I am. How about that? And it's Saturday!"

We talked as we marched on. I was having a difficult time getting the rednecks along the road to say anything to me, unless it was "fuck you, race traitor" or "go on back to Atlanta," or shit like that. Very unfriendly, but their reaction to all the national attention the march was bringing to their otherwise insulated lives had to be upsetting. Too fucking bad.

"So how did you wind up at WSB?" I asked Angela. "Are you a native Atlantan?"

"No. I grew up in Detroit. Went to Michigan State, got a couple of degrees and then decided to move here to the Black Mecca of America: the big A."

"A 'couple of degrees?'"

"Well, you know, black girl over-achiever and all that. That's what we have to do."

"In what? Your degrees."

"A Bachelor's in journalism and a Master's in psychology. I

still want to be a therapist. This radio gig is just for the money and the experience. What better way to get up close to the crazy than working in radio news?"

"Good point." The march had become more like a crawl, the massive crowd barely moving.

"So, maybe in a year or so I'll apply to Emory or Georgia State and try for my Ph.D. I could do clinical work now, but I want that word 'doctor' in front of my name. It means a lot. Especially to my family. My dad was a factory worker for forty years. He just retired two years ago from GM. He had to drop out of high school when he was sixteen and go to work. His dad, my grandpa, died from diabetes when he was forty. So, my dad had to work. He had seven brothers and sisters and my mom needed the help. After the Army, when he was twenty, he went into the factory and stayed there. It paid well, especially for a black man, so he worked days and nights and overtime when it was available, and he saved his money . . ." She abruptly stopped talking.

"What? Why'd you stop? What's the rest?" The march had slowed to a shuffle and stopped.

"Good Lord. Now you know more about me than WSB does!" She laughed. "See, normally we don't get all personal with white people about our business, our lives. Just tell 'em the bare facts. News, weather, traffic, so to speak. Stay quiet. Keep it all close. Hey, why do you think the march stopped?"

We both tried to see over the mass of people in front of us. Impossible. It seemed to go on forever. People around us began asking the same questions. Why are we stopped? What's going on? Is there trouble further ahead? Then, slowly, the march started moving again.

"Just a traffic back-up," someone said. "People traffic. No

trouble. We're okay." The morning chill had changed to a cloud of body heat hanging over the marchers.

"I think I understand why black folk avoid giving out too much personal info," I said, trying to keep the conversation going.

She turned to look at me. "Yeah? You think you understand? Really? So, tell me: Why are we so cautious with white folks?"

It was a challenge. It was clear she honestly doubted a white person could or wanted to understand anything about Blacks. The gulf between the two races was too wide, too deep. The mutual misunderstandings and suspicions and fears had become part of American culture, ingrained, and making any attempt at sorting it all out nearly impossible. The whites had always had the power, had always abused that power, had always had the privilege and the advantage of race, so much so and for so long it simply did not register with white people that this was the major cause of the anger and the resentment felt by blacks. It just didn't compute. The racist tropes and ugly comments that made up the average white person's opinion of blacks dug the gulf deeper, making the day-to-day frustration even more difficult to bear. And, it was there constantly. White privilege, white standards of beauty, success, achievement, security, endless reminders of white exceptionalism.

"Well," I began, "I grew up in an integrated neighborhood. I had black friends and white friends. We played together, went to school together, were Boy Scouts together, and in high school we even tried a bit of interracial dating. I played football my junior and senior years and half my teammates were black. I had a paper route from the time I was ten until I was fourteen and eventually most of my customers were black. Seriously, I do believe I understand all the crap black people have had to endure. The history of it all, anyway. I know about slavery and the Middle Passage and lynching and Jim Crow laws and the struggle for civil rights. So, for sure that means I get it. I know what makes Blacks keep their stories to themselves."

She said nothing for a moment. "Well?" I asked. "What do you think?" She turned to look at me and there was a momentary hesitation in her step. I thought she was going to stop walking and congratulate me for knowing so much about black folk, so much more than the average white person. She didn't.

She finally said, "Okay, let's play a game while we're walking. Have you ever seen one of those black women waiting for a bus in a white neighborhood? And, she's got two or three shopping bags sitting on the curb next to her and maybe it's raining, and she's got an umbrella but it's not a big one, so her bags are getting wet? And, she's wearing what looks like ratty old flat shoes or, worse yet, bedroom slippers and you can see her swollen ankles and feet are soaked. Ever seen that?"

"Sure. I've seen those women. And, I always feel sorry for them. They're stuck waiting to catch the bus that takes them home, out of the white neighborhoods. But, they're working, right? Trying to make their lives better, aren't they?"

"There's more to it than that. That woman isn't as old as she appears. In fact, she's probably got a couple of young kids at home waiting for her, kids who've been home alone since school got out four hours ago and the school bus dropped them off a couple of blocks from their apartment. She looks old because she's always worried. Waiting for that bus she's worried if her kids made it home safely. She's worried about what to prepare for supper, if there's anything in the pantry. She's worried because the youngest girl had a fever that morning and said her chest hurt and she's worried she doesn't have the money to get her to a doctor. And she's worried about the rent and the utility bills and she wishes she had a car, so it wouldn't take two hours to get to work in the morning and two hours to get home at night. But, she knows a car is something she'll probably never own. So, she stands there in the rain, her umbrella covering her head and shoulders while her legs and shoes are getting soaked. And, what do you suppose is in those shopping bags?"

"I don't know," I answered. "They always seem to be filled with something. And they look heavy."

"More than likely those bags are full of old clothing and household stuff her employer, the suburban white lady, no longer wants. So, in a gesture of charity and compassion she gives all those worn out, smelly shoes and faded blouses and sweaters with holes in them and maybe a few musty towels and washcloths, and two or three sheets, not a matching set but sheets that had been laying in the bottom of the white lady's linen closet for god knows how long, and, oh, yeah, two or three stained pillow cases to go with the sheets."

Angela's voice was becoming tighter as she spoke.

"Oh, and food. There's probably some food in those bags, too. Maybe the remains of a left-over baked ham that's been sitting in the white lady's refrigerator for a week or two, back behind some opaque Tupperware bowls and the lady finds it and thinks, 'I bet our Pearl would appreciate this ham. . .' and maybe some greasy, rigid fried chicken that she puts in the bag along with the ham. And, she does this because Pearl has been working for her family for three years and it's the Christian thing to do, help the poor and the sick and the homeless, even though Pearl has an apartment. And, now, standing in the rain, the ham is getting wet even though it's wrapped in plastic wrap and Pearl can smell the nasty, greasy chicken and, yes, she loves fried chicken, but the smell of wet, fried chicken is making her nauseous." Angela paused, waiting for me to comment. I couldn't.

We had reached the half-way point. Cumming was a little over a mile away. The road-side crowds of white hecklers were getting larger. A few empty beer cans were tossed into the slowly moving crowd, causing the marchers to duck their heads, hunch their shoulders. The taunts were becoming more and more raw, obscene, belligerent. *"Go home and fuck your black mama! Your old man's a pimp! . . . . Get the fuck off our road! . . . . White power! White power! Fuckin' niggers!. . . Martin Luther Coon's dead, you black assholes! You wanna be too?. . . . Let's shoot these niggers!"*

I looked at Angela. "Hey, this is getting dangerous. One of these assholes is going to throw something that hits us! Why don't we continue this conversation later?"

She shook her head. "I'm okay. Really. I'm not afraid of these people." We kept walking. "What I'm trying to say is you have no idea what black folk think, what we feel, how we get from day to day. I'm not trying to be sarcastic with you or patronizing, it's just that it's impossible for you to know what we experience. You're white. You got a pass when you were born." The pace of the march had picked up, and there were fewer rocks and cans being thrown at us.

A "pass?" That stung. I grew up in an attic with a violent father and a mother who had to leave when I was fourteen. But, I wanted to know what she meant.

"Okay, so how can whites ever get to the point where we do understand what you deal with?"

217

"You can't. Unless . . ." She paused and looked at me with an expression that I couldn't translate. Then . . . "Okay, my earnest radio co-worker. You want to understand and that's good. I appreciate that. Here's what you do: Go to work for a middle-class black family. That's right a black family. Take care of the kids while yours fend for themselves until you get home at night. Cook this black family's meals, watch their kids refuse food you would feed your kids in a second if you could afford to buy it. Your children would be glad to get a meal the black kids rejected. They'd be surprised that it wasn't the same fast-food garbage that so many times showed up on the kitchen table when you came home late, tired, too tired to help them with their school-work, too tired to hear about their day, and in a bad mood. "

As I listened, I tried to get the full visual of what she was saying. Imagining my working for a black family was difficult.

"Clean this black family's house," she continued. "Mop out their toilets. If they have old people living with them, a crippled-up Grandma or nearly-senile Grandpa, take care of them, too. First thing after you arrive, right after you've gulped down your egg McMuffin on the bus, lift their spindly legs and wash their butts, stained and crusty from the feces that seeped out of their diapers during the night. Try not to gag. Listen to them curse you. Change their sheets and put them back in bed where they'll stay until you arrive next morning to do it all again." Angela was trying to make her point without becoming angry. It wasn't working.

"Make yourself deaf, dumb, and blind when this black family has fights and arguments or when they use racial slurs to condemn those ignorant, uneducated whites who just moved in two blocks over. Who do they think they are, moving into

218

such a peaceful, clean, black neighborhood? What's next? Drug dealing on the corner? Gangs? White whores walking the streets so the kids can see? Why don't they stay in their neighborhoods where they belong? It's not our fault whites are so damned lazy and shiftless, you hear them say, and you stay silent for fear you'll scream at them and the anger will boil out of you in a white-hot rage, and you carry that anger with you all the time, no matter what you are doing it's there, churning and twisting until you develop malignant blood pressure, or diabetes, or you go psychotic and kill your own family! But, you stay silent."

At this point I wanted to stop her, tell her I understood what she was pointing out as an example of white unconsciousness. But, her intensity stopped me. I stayed silent, even as I heard an occasional, muffled "go ahead," or "keep talkin' sister," or "that's right," coming from whoever happened to be close to us and able to hear what Angela was saying. She continued as we shuffled along.

"And, do this for years. Day in and day out while you learn everything there is to learn about blacks and their prejudices and their secrets and how much they fear and despise you, and all the things you must do to show the proper deference, because black rage could erupt at any moment and you could be killed. Study hard, because this is information you must have if you are to survive. And, don't forget to stand aside when you and a black person approach the same door at the grocery store at the same time, a grocery store you rode two buses to get to, and the black woman only had to drive three blocks in her SUV to get to the same store. Do that, let that black woman pass in front of you until it becomes second nature, like breathing. Because if you push ahead of her, if you don't let her enter before you do, you'll get that 'look' that says, 'how dare you, whitey, how dare you enter ahead of me. Know your place.' All of that in just a look. And, maybe, she'll say the 'C' word under her breath, just loud enough so only you hear it."

"'C' word?"

"Cracker. "

"And watch the news where the guy says maybe a grocery store is going to open soon in your decimated neighborhood because a local college professor has identified where you live as a 'food desert.' A *food desert!* Like you really don't live in America, you live in . . . where? A white Somalia? A Caucasian Bangladesh? And this constant emotional pain just keeps up and keeps up until you want to die from the shame and the hurt and the awful realization that because you're white you are condemned to be invisible unless you commit a crime or make a fuss about the horrors you live with. Only then do you become visible and at the same moment, a target."

For all the attention I was paying to the march at this point, we might as well have been standing still in the middle of this rural two-lane road. Angela's words were registering for sure. I didn't know that much about her before we came to this demonstration. Just the little bit you pick up when you and your co-workers are in an intense environment like broadcast news. You can form quick bonds of solidarity, especially in a profession that is targeted by right wing lunatics who refuse to believe anything they cannot measure with their basic five senses. So, I just kept silent and listened.

"And, get used to the idea that your home, your apartment, or your rented house, is falling apart and is going to stay that way. The plumbing works sporadically and the company that manages the apartment complex for some foreign investors, or the hateful black man who owns your house, and won't keep things working and won't exterminate the roaches and rats and remove the black mold off the bathroom floor. But, you must deal with it all and get back to work next morning for that black family who haven't a clue about what you endure day after day." I looked at her again, expecting to see anger and pain spread across her face. Instead, she was half-smiling, a sardonic lift to the corners of her mouth.

"Jesus, Angela, I had no idea. I never gave race that much thought. "

"And that's my point; sadly, white people never think about this stuff. They can't. It's outside anything they ever have or ever will experience. That's another reason these fools yelling 'nigger' and 'nigger lover' at us are so contemptible. They live nasty, empty little lives but believe because they're white they have an unchallenged claim to racial superiority, to a higher level in the pecking order than blacks. So, they carry their shameful battle flags and wear their pointy white hoods and demand to be recognized as better than blacks, even if they only went as far as tenth grade and have travelled no further from their homes than forty miles down the highway to Atlanta. The black woman leading this march attended Antioch College in Yellow Springs, Ohio, and the New England Conservatory of Music in Boston. But, the high-school drop-outs cursing her this morning believe they are her superiors, that she is nothing but an ignorant creature not far removed from the jungles of Africa."

Her voice had softened, muted by an undertone of sadness. We both looked to the right where a raggedy white man was waving his Stars and Bars as though he was signaling for someone to rescue him from some approaching terror. He leaned back and let loose with what he must have thought was an intimidating Rebel yell so fierce it would cause the marchers to scatter and flee in panic. With his mouth wide open we could see his toothless pink gums right about the time his "*Yeeeeeee . . .*" segued into "*. . . Hawwwwwwww.*" The people around him were gleefully pumping their fists in the air, like they would if the local high school football team had just scored a touchdown.

"And," Angela went on, "there's always the question of 'why.' Why do so many whites in this country see blacks so negatively? Look at those people with the flag. What is that? What did we do to cause such fear and suspicion and contempt? We didn't ask to be brought here. We had no choice. We were slaves. What choice does a slave have? What did we do when we got here? We worked. We built fortunes for whites with our forced labor. We were a critical component in the rise of the US from being a frontier civilization to becoming the world's strongest economic power. So, maybe it's guilt. Maybe every time a white American looks at a black American he senses the truth that so much of what this country became and so much of how whites have benefitted from that, came as a result of that transfer of forced labor into material wealth and built family fortunes, fortunes that went to whites, not us. Remember that '40-acres and a mule' we were promised? Maybe that guilt has sunk to a cellular level in whites where it can never be removed, never be understood, and never, never accepted. Maybe that's it, my curious white marching buddy."

In the distance we could hear the dissonant sound of trumpets blaring and snare drums being beaten with no thought given to actual rhythm or music. The blasting sound was coming from a crowd of counter-demonstrators who were trying to drown out the speeches that were about to begin. The front of the march was in the town square, the leaders standing on the steps of the Forsyth County Courthouse. Spread around them, spilling out from the courthouse grounds and into the streets was the vanguard of the massive crowd of demonstrators whose numbers stretched back two miles to the strip mall where the march had begun. Those thousands now crowded into the town square would be the only marchers able to hear the messages of determination from the civil rights leaders who had been saying the same words, giving the same speeches, enduring the same insults and beatings and jailings and dog attacks for decades.

But, hearing the speeches was not the point of the march. Who in this crowd of 20-thousand had not heard the words over and over again? The point was to show a small slice of the solidarity that existed among so many millions of white and black Americans in partial contradiction to what Angela had said; to show the shared belief in justice and equal respect; equal opportunity, and equal protection under the law. Someday, perhaps, the bigotry and racism and fear would end. Someday, maybe, a sense of justice and respect would awaken in the whites and the terrible disrespect they had shown to their dark-skinned brothers and sisters also would end. As Dr. King had cried out over the National Mall in Washington, D.C. in 1963, *"I still have a dream, a dream deeply rooted in the American dream – that one day this nation will rise up to its creed, 'We hold these truths to be self-evident; that all men are created equal.'. . . I have a dream that my four little children will one day live in a nation where they will not be judged by the color of their skin, but by the content of their character. I have a dream today."*

Some day that dream might be realized. But, August 28,

1963, was not that day. And, on January 25, 1987 – twenty-four years later and here in Forsyth County, Georgia, – it still was not that day.

Angela's disorienting lecture of how I might get a true sense of being black in America, and how blacks understood whites to a far greater degree than whites would ever understand blacks, stayed with me after the Forsyth County march. It reminded me of the book "Black Like Me" written by white journalist John Griffin and published in the early 1960s. After a regimen of exposure to ultraviolet light, skin dyes, and oral medication provided by a New Orleans shoe shiner, Griffin eventually looked in the mirror and saw a black man looking back. What he experienced hitchhiking in the Deep South after he became "black" was shocking. While he expected to meet the racism he knew existed, he was not prepared for the depth of the hatred and insults directed at him in Mississippi and Alabama. The whites treated him as if he were sub-human, a creature exempt from common decency.

While Angela's thought experiment had given me a deeper sense of the black experience in a culture founded on racism and genocide, it was not even close to Griffin's direct encounter with the pain and contempt forced on black Americans daily, hourly, always. Slowly, what she told me began to fade. Within days of the march it had begun to morph into simply a story of the hardships faced by African-Americans, as though they, like other immigrant ethnic groups had come to America looking for that new life, had to go through a process of assimilation in order to adapt to their new country, which was bullshit thinking and I knew it. Assimilation? They had tried for three centuries without success. They were not allowed to assimilate. They were consigned to an existence that seemed a parody of life lived by whites, but in a grotesque way that usually ended in frustration and shame and often, with horrific regularity, violence and death.

I had been trying to weave into my nightly program the reality of what African-Americans were faced with day after day, year after year, but it wasn't having the effect I was hoping for. I began sounding like a white professor giving a lecture to a sociology class on the evils of racism. A class of privileged white students who, led by a privileged white professor, would complete the course, get their grades, eventually graduate, and move effortlessly into the rhythms of white America, never missing a beat and convinced they understood racism because of a one-semester class on race relations. They honestly believed they would never be a part of racist America while, in fact, their daily lives had been programmed to perpetuate the same attitudes and actions they claimed to have left behind in Professor Whoever's sociology class.

Station management decided to remind me I was an entertainer, not a professor, and that it was time to get off the race topic and on to what my Program Director called "contemporary topics." The irony, or stupidity, of what he said was totally lost on him. So, onward to contemporary topics. Like the gay-bashing that was occurring while Atlanta's gay community was being devastated by the AIDS epidemic. Or the Israeli/Palestinian crisis that had suddenly morphed into the first *intifada*. These were my suggestions, of course, since my PD didn't have a clue about either topic except for the reports in the Atlanta newspapers which offered little more than casualty figures; the number of dead among Atlanta's creative community, the "fact" that it was gay sex that unleashed this death wave; the intransigence of the Palestinian Arabs who were unwilling to cooperate in their own annihilation; the brutality of the Israel Defense Forces who had no hesitation in using live ammunition against elementary school students who insisted on throwing rocks at IDF Armed Personnel Carriers. The IDF was charged with ending the disorder that was becoming a full-blown insurrection, by any means necessary. One of those "means" was labeled "might, power, and beatings," which included "breaking Palestinian bones." Images of Israeli soldiers beating and shooting Palestinian teenagers were televised around the world and resulted in the IDF's adoption of rubber bullets, mis-named because they were regular rounds with a rubber coating. They could still kill, just not as frequently. And, that was the objective: injure, wound, maim, cause unbearable pain. Only the death toll would make it onto the night's news. Broken legs, arms, collar bones, who cared? The victims were only Palestinians who, in addition to the violence, had to endure the insults: *"Your mother the whore." "Your son belongs in the ground." "Your family eats the dung of goats."* Violence by the IDF was considered "protecting our borders." Rock throwing by Palestinian ten-year-old children was "terrorism."

Chapter 19

Christians

It's late summer, 1987. I'm sitting at a café table in the station's break room. Sitting across from me is a terrorism expert from the Atlanta Police Department, Lieutenant Darius Frazier. He has a serious look on his face and an open note pad on the table in front of him. The cup of coffee I poured for him when he arrived is sitting there getting cold.

Our meeting was arranged after WSB received its second bomb threat in less than a month. A series of death threats, left on my voice-mail, were more focused and certainly more personal. They detailed how I was to be killed. Station management laughed those off. The attitude was, individual death threats? *Meh.* Comes with being a liberal broadcaster in the deep South. A bomb threat against the building!? *Holy shit! Call the police!!!!*

The threats were the result of what I had been recently focusing on, a metastasizing cancer called the Christian Re-construction Movement. An active branch of these crazed religionists had opened in Cobb County, the same county that had given the country the political careers of Newt Gingrich,

Bob Barr, and ol' Lester Maddox, the chicken restaurant owning, crazy-ass, axe-handle carrying former governor of Georgia. The axe handle? That was to threaten the black folk who felt they had a legal right to go sit in ol' Lester's restaurant and order lunch.

I was fully aware that Cobb County was, and always had been, a locus of violent Southern racism and bigotry. It also was a center of ugly Christian hate, hate that was directed not only toward the usual suspects, i.e., gays, immigrants, Jews, and people of color, but also anyone who did not share the toxic religious bullshit that was the motivation behind it all. One of the more insane religious cults that had burrowed its way into the area was Christian Reconstructionism, a fundamentalist movement invented by a true sociopath named Rousas Rushdoony, an Armenian-American son of immigrants whose ancestors had for hundreds of years lived in a remote area near the Biblical Mount Ararat. The family claimed that each generation going back 1600 years had produced a Christian priest or mystic. Rousas was the most recent.

The cult was centered in California and it was in Los Angeles in 1965 that Rushdoony founded an organization called the Chalcedon Foundation the sole purpose of which was to return humanity to a pre-Enlightenment, medieval view of a "God-centered" world. Science be damned; reason be damned; logic be damned; Rushdoony's world view was far more perverted and corrupt than any of the political "isms" competing for the human body and mind. All at once, I found I was a target of these freaks because of what I was talking about on my program.

I had long ago concluded that religion was much worse than Marx's admonition that . . . "religion . . . is the opium of the masses." Opium is an addictive narcotic that will not only put you to sleep, but also, used incautiously, will kill you. Religion, however, will destroy your mind, make you insane, fill your head with visions of demons and angels locked in mortal combat, eat away your self-confidence, self-respect, and self-worth, all to be replaced by a sense of horror as to what will happen when you die if you don't completely accept the dictates of the demon-haunted world to which religion will introduce you. Religion is fear. Religion teaches one who to hate, who to destroy, who is condemned, who is beyond redemption. Opium? Opium was dreams.

Among those beyond redemption, especially in the bullshit temples of Christian Reconstruction? Gay folk, of course. And a whole assemblage of targets beyond gays, to be sure, but gays? They were to be fried in the hottest bowels of Hell. Of course, religion has been used as the excuse for the slaughter of innocent men, women and children since the entire obscene enterprise began. Consider, among countless examples, the burning of "witches," the frequent Inquisitions, the various Crusades, the silence of the Catholic Church while the Nazis slaughtered millions of Jews, the genocide of Native People when Christianity arrived with the intent to subjugate, enslave, and destroy cultures older than Christianity itself, after, of course the required charade of bringing Jesus to the savage masses. The list of religious mass murder and cultural destruction is endless and ongoing. And, here I was, less than 25 miles from the Southeast headquarters of the murderous sewage known as Christian Reconstruction.

The death threats began shortly after I started focusing on the AIDS epidemic in general, and the vicious attitude toward gays in particular, an attitude that increased in intensity as the plague devastated ever larger populations of gay men. And, it was quickly determined where the threats were coming from: Cobb County. Since, the Christian Reconstruction headquarters for the Southeast was located there, it was easy to conclude that the cult was responsible.

Gay men are an active or passive target of nearly all branches of the Abrahamic religions. Oddly, lesbians, not so much, and there's a simple explanation: the voyeuristic male thrill − whether the man is Christian or not − in watching women have sex together. It's an obsession that dwells in the id of most men. And, it can reach crazy extremes, such as the male conviction that if two women are seen leaving, say, a coffee shop together they must be on their way to the nearest motel for an afternoon of hot girl-sex before going home to prepare dinner for hubby and the kids.

After clearing my decision with station management, I contacted the Atlanta Police Department to report the threats. At first, their response was practically zero. "We're familiar with your program, Mr. Malloy, and given the nature of your topics it's not surprising that you'd get that sort of reaction. This is Georgia, right? The buckle of the Bible Belt, right? So, you might want to just ignore those phone messages and mark it up to some religious type who's having a bad reaction to what you're saying. However, if it continues, give us a call back and we'll check it out. The detective you'll want to talk to if that happens is Lt. Frazier, Darius Frazier. You might want to write that down."

The threats continued. I'll admit the nut-balls making the threats were certainly creative in describing the violence they were planning to deliver to me and anyone who happened to be in my immediate vicinity when the Wrath Of God came roaring down from heaven in a roiling, ear-drum bursting wall of fire. Wow! Great imagery. Of course, my attitude was fuck 'em. Their entire story was ridiculous bullshit to begin with, and fear of a horde of religious assholes simply was not going to cause me to feel any anxiety or sense of danger. At least, not at first.

But, then, the threats got more graphic: the station would be bombed and collapse in a shuddering pile of smoking rubble! The death toll would be enormous! God would prevail!! And, all this simply because I was advocating for equal justice, equal protection, for people who happened to be gay? In Atlanta? The Gay Mecca of the South? In 1987? I was aware there is nothing on earth more capable of destruction than the violence inherent in religion, especially the Christian religion. History is waist-deep in the river of blood caused by Christian violence. Jesus? Forget Jesus. The Christians certainly have, except for the hideously violent return of their Messiah as written in Revelation. Their religion has devolved once again into the form most recognizable by non-Christians: a weapon, a threat, extreme violence, contempt for the earth, anti-woman, a desire for global destruction that will please their god and return his son to what's left of humanity. This is some sick shit, no question.

After the second bomb threat and the second evacuation of the station, the Atlanta Police Department decided it was time to take it all seriously. But, as is the case with cowards, after a report in the local press, the bomb threats stopped. Not, however, the promise to deal with me in the same manner the Denver radio talk show host, Alan Berg, had been dealt with by the Christian White Supremacists in Colorado: assassination as he arrived home after work one night. Of course, my

231

attitude was bring it on assholes, which was probably not the best response to religious sewer-dwellers out to eliminate one more pagan voice who saw their religious bullshit as true religious bullshit and was talking about it on a (*gasp!*) 50-thousand-watt radio station that reached half the country!

The APD's Lieutenant Frazier got serious. "Look, these people are completely dedicated to their extreme beliefs, especially the Christian Reconstruction ideas. So far as we know they have not committed any violence, no arson, no murders. Other than the threats, they haven't done anything that calls for more than the surveillance we keep them under constantly. And regarding the threats, if we can find those responsible we will arrest them. But, you need to understand these types of domestic terrorists. They are capable of all sorts of violence. They claim to be Christian fundamentalists. They are not. That's their cover story. Claiming to be a church or a religious organization gives them a certain amount of protection under the Constitution and from the IRS. But their claim is bogus." He paused a moment, looking at me intently with that cop look that can scare the hell out of you, even when your worst crime is jaywalking. It's a cop thing.

"Do you own a weapon," he asked? "Preferably a hand gun?"

"Uh . . .no. I used to, years ago. But, not now.

"Have you ever had firearms training? Like in the military?"

"No."

He shuffled some papers. "Are you afraid to use a weapon or have one in your home?"

"No." I was getting images of hordes of Christian Soldiers (like in the hymn) attacking through the backyard, guns blazing, me picking them off one at a time . . . *pow! pow! pow! Yeee-haw!!!*

"How do you feel about carrying one on your person?"

Hot damn! Carrying a firearm? Like the old West?

"Yeah," I answered. "I can do that."

"All right," Frazier said. "Here's the drill. We'll do a background check on you and, if you pass, send you to the police firing range to be trained in how to safely use a weapon . . ."

I grinned, "And how to kill somebody, right?" For a moment Frazier didn't answer. He filled in some forms, got my signature, and told me an APD instructor would be in touch. "Hope it doesn't come to that, okay?" he said, as I walked with him to the exit. And with that, he left. He never touched his coffee.

In addition to arming me, for the next few weeks the Atlanta cops had a patrol car waiting at the station's employee exit each night at 1-AM to escort me to my pickup truck which was parked not more than 50 yards away. But, who knew what evil religious or racist thug might be lurking somewhere in the shadows of those 50 yards? It was beginning to feel like some sort of insane melodrama. Will Mike get shot tonight? Tomorrow night? I was over all of it, and it was starting to creep me out to the max. I wanted to detach from all the threats and talk of violence and just chill out. I knew where to go.

Chapter 20

Witches

A fixture on one of the residential side streets in mid-town Atlanta was a small café called The Grove. It had opened sometime in the early 70s and had become a gathering place for a segment of the city's community that I found fascinating, but about which I was mostly ignorant: Wiccans. I had gotten into the habit of stopping in late at night, after midnight, for a cup of honey-flavored orange tea and the pastry *de la nuit.* The gathering room was lit by a circle of candles on each of seven tables. There were several tall pillar candles placed on a counter that extended across the far side of the room. Behind the counter, a wide door that was always open to the kitchen where the owner – Lady Galadriel – prepared and served the specialties of the house. In a corner there was a small fireplace that, in the winter, added a comforting warmth, a welcoming glow that could be seen from the street outside through a large scratched and opaque window.

In a room that adjoined the main chamber – also lit by an abundance of flickering candles - her partner, Tinker, designed and made pieces of silver jewelry; finger rings, neck chains, ear rings, bracelets, and Wiccan medallions that were museum quality. Occasionally, I would sit on a stool near his work space and watch him create his exquisite charms. He worked in silence and it was understood that entering his space meant no talking, no conversation, nothing but silence perforated by the slight silvery sounds coming from the metal tools he used. If he knew you, he would smile and whisper, "merry meet and blessed be" as you settled yourself to watch his artistry.

One night, I noticed a flyer sitting on one of the tables, apparently left there by an earlier customer. I picked it up and in the muted light read the announcement of an upcoming Wiccan convention scheduled for early fall. The convention was one in a series of periodic gatherings of the practitioners of Wicca, this one to be held in the North Georgia mountains. The invitation was clear in who could attend: Wiccans only. And maybe a writer, I thought? In addition to my radio gig, I also freelanced for several Atlanta alternative publications, social justice weeklies and an occasional piece for the *Atlanta Journal-Constitution*'s Sunday magazine.

Soto voce, I asked Tinker if he knew who I could contact to get permission to attend the convention. "You come in here a lot, right?" he asked. The only noise, other than our brief conversation, was the slight hissing of the Bunsen burner he was using to soften a small globe of silver.

"I do," I answered. "Love the tea and the cheesecake. And the quiet. It's soul refreshing."

Without looking up from his work, he scribbled on a piece of paper and slid it towards me.

"Thank you."

"Enjoy. And, blessed be."

The next day I called the number on the slip of paper Tinker had given me. The person's name was Bronwen.

At first, Bronwen was hesitant to talk to me, reluctant even to admit her name. Wiccans in the South are considered witches in the old-world sense of sorceresses, spell casters, evil women like Shakespeare's three witches:

When shall we three meet again?
In thunder, lightning, or in rain
When the hurly-burly's done,
When the battle's lost and won. . .
Fair is foul, and foul is fair:
Hover through the fog and filthy air.
Like that.

However, once I mentioned Tinker, and after a few phone pleasantries on my part and pointed questions from her about my interest, and my swearing on all things Wiccan that I was not a media spy, not looking for a tabloid-style expose of witches and spells, she said she would talk with the others in her Circle and let me know later in the day. Before she ended the conversation with an almost cheery "*blessed be,*" she said there would be no photographs allowed of the convention participants. And, certainly no photos of the ritual nude dancing that is part of the Wiccan celebrations of *Beltane* or *Eostar,* or any one of the holy days that celebrate the seasons, the moon, and the mother of all things, the Earth.

Sure enough, that evening she called back.

"Why do you want to come to this convention? Tell me again. What is your intent?"

I answered her honestly. "To learn."

"To learn . . . what? How to cast spells? How to do magick?"

"Well, no. I want to learn about your beliefs, about Wicca,

about your history. I'm very curious and there is so much I don't know."

"Are there not books, hundreds of books, written about us? Can you not go to the library and find all you want to know?"

"Yes, there are," I answered. "But they are all written from a certain perspective, even the books written by Wiccans can be obscure, cryptic. That's not what I want." This interview – if that's what it was - was not going well. There was no way I could just come out and say I wanted to know their secrets. I wanted to see things the way they saw things. And the focus on feminine energy and feminine power, and the fact that whatever that power was, it made me uncomfortable. That's what I wanted to understand, the power. But, I was hesitant to come right out and say what I really wanted from Wicca.

I tried again. "Look, it's more than just learning; I want to feel Wiccan energy, absorb what I might see, come away from your gathering with, well, an understanding, something I don't have now."

Bingo! I had hit on exactly the right words: Experience, learning, and the big one, understanding. I was in, and in addition to feeling good about being accepted, I also had a fleeting *frisson* of uncertainty; what door had I just opened? What would be waiting when I walked through? Maybe nothing. Maybe just *antici-pointment.* As in big build-up, bigger let-down.

The gathering was to be held deep inside the Chattahoochee National Forest, in a valley near a slope of the Appalachian Mountain range as it passes through Georgia. The area is called *Unicoi*, a Cherokee word that means "white." It refers to the low-lying clouds and the thick fog that can envelop the area. The surrounding natural beauty is spectacular, especially during Autumn when the oaks, red maples, sugar maples, hickory, and beech trees all explode in a palette of intense red, yellow, burgundy, lavender, and orange, a cascade of color that stops you in your tracks no matter how many times you've seen it.

Registration and check-in at the Unicoi Lodge was scheduled for early evening Friday. After settling in, a welcoming ceremony would be led, according to the schedule, by a Lord and Lady. Then a casual meet-and-greet to give the participants a chance to re-connect or meet for the first time. The Saturday schedule was packed with workshops, the proper use of herbs, lectures, discussions, and elements of Wiccan rituals designed to instruct the newest members of the different covens. Sunday would be more of the same, with time set aside for walks through the mountains, meditation, and classes the most effective ways to conduct the rituals just learned. Sunday night included a Waning Moon Festival to be held a mile from the event's central location, up a trail and through the forest, to a site where logs had been stacked within a fire circle in anticipation of the celebration. And after the waning moon ritual, a proper Wiccan feast. Monday was departure day after one last family get-together under the trees.

As I studied the packet of information the check-in person had given me - a large manila envelope with two tiny stars in the upper left-hand corner - a round, purple disc slipped out and clattered to the floor. It was about the size of the lid on a large Mason jar and on the back a clip-pin had been fixed.

"Hey, don't lose that," one of the men pushing a luggage cart said as he walked by. "That's your protection. You have to pin it to your robe or whatever you'll be wearing while we're all together here."

"Protection? From what? Ghosts? Banshees?" Oops. Wrong choice of words. My first fuck-up.

He stopped pushing the cart and looked at me. "No, not banshees. From each other. Hey, you must be new. Where you from?"

"Atlanta. Local guy. So, what do you mean 'from each other?'

"Are you with one of the Atlanta covens?"

"Actually, no. I'm here to write about the convention. You know, an observer." Second oops. He looked at me with pointed curiosity and a shadow of suspicion.

So, I went through the questions again, his questions, basically the same ones Bronwen had asked, until my new acquaintance was satisfied I wasn't there to write something trite or demeaning. "That's what usually happens when someone writes about us," he said. His name was Cadmun. He said it was an Anglo-Saxon name meaning "warrior" and he was the High Priest of a coven in Montana. His counterpart, the coven's High Priestess, also was his wife.

It hadn't occurred to me that witches could, or would, get married. Marriage seemed counter to the idea of absolute freedom that I thought was at the center of Wicca. That meant that Lady Galadriel and Tinker at The Grove probably were married, too. This was starting to feel like a "Leave it to Beaver" episode from the 50s, if Ward and June had been leaders of a coven.

"My wife, Lady Glenys, that's her over there talking to the woman with the crazy hair, she started our coven before I met her," he said, chatting as though he'd known me for years. "In fact, we met at one of her Circles. I was there to learn how to trance and we talked for a while and *pow!* That Wicca Magick

239

kicked in and, eventually, we got married."

"So, the term 'Lady' means the woman is the leader of the coven?" I asked.

"Co-leader. There's also the male 'Lord' of the group. We believe in a true gender-equal culture. So, I'm a witch, too. Not a wizard, not a warlock; a witch."

"Interesting for sure, uh, Cadmun. But, the purple disc. You said it's for protection. From what, exactly? I'm not sure what you mean by 'each other.' And, what about these two stars in the corner?" I held out the packet so he could see them.

"Well, I'm not sure about the stars. I'll find out for you. But, wearing the disc lets each witch know everyone is here in peace, no one is looking for a power contest, no one is presenting a challenge. If the disc were red, it would mean the one wearing it was looking for some sort of confrontation. Witches will do that just for sport. Some people play bridge; we get into these ridiculous power struggles. Like, who has the best magick, who knows the most occult incantations. It's all sort of silly, but it can cause grudges and that's not a good thing for witches. A witch grudge can lead to all sorts of dangerous stuff, believe me. So, the purple disc will let others know you're not a threat. And, if there are any unconscious challenges thrown toward you by accident, the disc will absorb that dark energy and dissipate it. In other words, wear the disc and you're safe." So, the purple discs were not just ornamental. "I'll see you then at the opening ceremony tonight?" Cadmun was definitely a friendly witch. "Yeah, see you then," I answered.

I found the room I was assigned to and unpacked. A window near the bed looked out into a dark pine forest that surely was the home of faeries, sprites, and all sorts of wee folk, some of whom, I guessed had serrated teeth, and maybe didn't particularly care for humans, witches or otherwise. I made a quick mental note: Don't go walking in the Unicoi Forest after dark. Alone.

Not that I would, of course.

The welcoming ceremony was to be held in the Lodge's central gathering spot: A large circular room with a massive fire pit built into the floor in the room's center. Suspended on chains above the pit, a huge stacked rock chimney, shaped like a pyramid, that inhaled the smoke and exhaled it through a large ceramic pipe embedded in the ceiling. Surrounding the pit were concentric circles of padded folding chairs. No matter where one sat, the view of the fire pit and the speaker, if there was one, was unobstructed. Placed near the pit was a large round wooden table with an odd collection of items that immediately got my attention. In the table's center, a pentagram had been burned into the wood. On each side of the pentagram stood a statue, on one side a male (the God), on the other, the female (Goddess). There was a small stone bowl holding salt next to an identical bowl holding water. A censer held several sticks of unlit incense. Lying parallel to each other, an elaborately designed double-edged dagger and an oak wand. The whole tableau was curious and more than a bit Medieval. The ceremony was not going to start for another thirty minutes so I stepped outside into the Autumn night to look at the stars. They were especially bright and filled the sky and the dark spaces among the tops of the pine trees with a soft light. A warm, light breeze blew around me and I thought of the Moody Blues lyric " . . . *breathe deep the gathering gloom . . . watch light fade from every room . . .*"

The air was moving against my bare arms, feeling like the flow of a slow stream that gently pushed me alongside the lodge to the rear of the building, toward the deep black woods. As I turned the corner I heard a faint melodic humming and, at the same time, caught flashes of white just inside the edge of the forest, ephemeral light that moved around the base of the trees, moving left, then right, around and around. I walked closer and saw the floating shapes of three young women. They were whirling around a decaying tree stump on which sat several lighted candles, their bodies bending and swaying to the humming sound that rose and fell as they circled. I stood in the darkness watching, fascinated. As they danced, they slowly let the robes they were wearing – the flashes of white I had seen – slide from their bodies, until they were naked. The dance gained intensity with their arms rising and falling, their heads moving side to side. They were the source of the humming and now it got louder, insistent. As they turned and twisted in front of me, one took my hand and pulled me into the undulating circle. She whispered, "Remove your clothing. Remove your identity. Remove the weight. Make yourself free. Dance with us." And, I did. My clothing dropped to the ground as each piece came off; jacket, shirt, jeans, underwear, shoes, socks, free!

The forest floor was soft and loamy and sensual against my bare soles. Two of the dancers each took one of my hands and pulled me closer. I had an intense feeling of flight, that I was levitating, flying through the night, my naked guides leading me through the pines, taking me to the tops of the nearby mountains, diving crazily back to the ground, swinging up again, accelerating, the air rushing past in a cool torrent, almost visible.

And then, it stopped. I was again on the ground, clothed, breathing rapidly. As the three women walked away into the darkness in their white tunics, one said, in a melodic voice, that the welcoming ceremony was about to begin and perhaps it was time we all went inside. *So mote it be.*

The room was about half-filled with conference attendees, most of whom were relatively young and mostly female. The conversations were animated and filled with *"merry meet!"* and *"blessed be!"* as one more familiar face was seen and greeted. I didn't feel like questioning what had just happened outside in the night. Just accept it and be grateful. My three dancing companions moved across the room to join friends. I stood there for a moment trying to decide if I should follow and sit with them or find a seat where I was standing. Suddenly, I was enveloped in an invisible cloud of Chole. The perfume. It's seductive quality nails me every time. For a moment I felt immobilized, pleasantly rooted to the spot. Then I noticed a woman sitting alone near the center of the circle of chairs. She was looking directly at me, with deep green eyes that I couldn't turn away from. She made a slight wave with her hand, the one lying across the back of the chair next to her, a barely discernable motion inviting me to come sit next to her. It couldn't have been clearer to me if she had shouted. I made my way through the chairs toward her, realizing I was following the scent of Chloe. It was hers. The closer to her, the more powerful the fragrance. I slid into the chair next to her.

"Hi, or merry meet, take your pick," she said, half-smiling. "My name is Anita. What, pray tell, is yours?"

The green eyes had me in total lock-down. And her black hair, deep black, blue black. And her crimson lips. Fiery. Slightly open. And her black denim jeans. And the deep green pull-over that perfectly matched her eyes. Oh, my goodness.

"Mike . . . my name is Mike. Hi."

"So. Come here often?" She asked. Perfect. No other way to say 'hello' at a Wicca convention. I laughed.

"I like that. 'Come here often. . .? ' Actually, no. First time. How about you?"

"Well, in truth, there's nothing like getting together with a bunch of witches to purge your mind, re-order your aura, align your *chi*, balance your check-book."

Once again, she made me laugh. "You are funny. I love it!"

Her smile deepened. "Where do you call home?" she asked.

"Atlanta."

"Really! Me, too," she said. "I live near Emory Medical Center."

"I'm staying in the Druid Hills neighborhood," I said, lightly skimming the irony of the name. "So, you're a witch . . .? I mean Wiccan? Okay, obviously you are, or you wouldn't be here, right?"

She leaned toward me. The Chloe was intoxicating. "How could you guess? I thought I was keeping it secret." she whispered.

"Are you a good witch or a bad witch," I asked, realizing I had just stolen the question Dorothy uses when she first meets Glinda.

She laughed. "Sometimes both?" It came out as a question. "But, I'm here, I guess you'd say, to hone my skills. These gatherings have a way of re-charging the psychic batteries. So, tonight I'm an observer."

"Surprise! So am I!" I said. And, again, her smile swept over me, this time causing my skin to react as if from a mild electric charge, sort of . . . *tingly.*

The room grew suddenly silent. We both turned toward the fire pit. Whispers, just spoken, floated to the rafters and fell, fluttering around us like dying moths. Someone touched a gong, the sound soft and light. The welcoming ceremony had begun. The room's lights dimmed, almost out. The fire in the pit flared and crackled. Two people appeared from opposite sides of the room and approached the table, a man and a woman, both wearing flowing robes that folded around them. His was the color of burnt acorns. Hers, a royal purple that glowed as she moved in the firelight. They stood silently, breathing together deeply, an unspoken invitation for the audience to join them in this meditation. We did. The minutes passed. The room itself was breathing. The woman stepped forward and placed several lighted sticks of incense into *the censer.*

"I cleanse and consecrate thee," she began, *"burning incense, as representing the element Air. May your essence bless us and bring your clarity to our circle. So mote it be."* She moved the bowl of salt to the center of the table. *"I cleanse and consecrate thee, bowl of salt, as representing the element Earth. May your essence bless us and bring your stability to our circle. So mote it be."*

The man stepped forward and placed a lighted candle near the center of the table and said, *"I cleanse and consecrate thee, candle flame, as representing of the element Fire. May your essence bless us and bring your passion to our circle. So mote it be."*

He lifted the bowl of water and placed it near the center of the table. *"I cleanse and consecrate thee, bowl of water, as representing the element Water. May your essence bless us and bring intuition to our circle. So mote it be."*

I turned my head slightly to look at Anita, to see how she was taking these welcoming ceremony incantations. Her eyes were half-closed, the long lashes thick and dark. Her head was slightly bowed. Her cheekbones etched a curve that I wanted to touch. Her hair dropped behind her shoulders. Her breathing was deep and slow, and each inhale and exhale lifted and lowered her breasts under the forest green sweater. An indescribable rush of desire flowed into me so intense I thought I might faint, pass out, fall on my ass, and then try to explain that, no, nothing's the matter, really, I just had my soul jolted. Happens all the time. Sorry.

But, I couldn't move. Not even to faint.

The Lord and Lady continued the opening ritual with their chants and mumbles. I wanted to listen, to understand what they were saying so I could write it all down later. But, as they went on, I lost them completely and, instead, tried to center the thoughts flying around inside my mind like bats, diving, rising, twisting.

And, then, raising the wand, the woman began casting or closing the circle she had bound around us. This, I remember.

"Lady of the Moon, of the fertile Earth and rolling seas,

You who are the Maiden, with strong heart and youthful spirit,

You who are the Mother, with able body and nurturing spirit,

You who are the Crone, with wise mind and compassionate spirit,

You who are birth, life, love and death,

You who are north, south, east and west,

The boundary and the center, within us and without us,

Descend upon my circle, I pray, to witness these rites in your honor.

Then the man raised the dagger and began his incantation:

"Lord of the Sun, of the sky and the wild,

You who are the Consort, with amorous heart and lusty spirit,

You who are the Hunter, with robust body and cunning spirit,

You who are the Father, with thoughtful mind and guiding spirit,
You who are the birth, life, love, and death,
You who are the north, south, east and west,
The boundary and the center, within us and without us,
Descend upon my circle, I pray, to witness these rites in your
honor."

A chorus of "*so mote it be*" filled the room and we knew we were under the protection of both the Lord and the Lady, the Goddess and the God. The opening ceremony was complete.

It certainly was more intense than a Wednesday night Baptist prayer meeting.

The lights came back up and the room once again filled with conversations and greetings. Off to one side a table had been set for the welcoming feast. In the background, New Age-y harpsichord music added to the Medieval feel of the affair I had noticed earlier, as the now-consecrated witches partook of the various dishes and bowls of foods and desserts. As for drinks, there was a choice: An endless supply of wine or jugs of "honey-wine," the ancient libation, mead.

Anita and I were still seated.

"Care to join the feast?" I asked, hoping the answer would be no. The feeling that had pushed through me like a tsunami had begun to subside.

"Actually, no. But, a walk would be wonderful. The night is so cool and clear. Shall we?" Asking me to walk with her was totally unnecessary. *Not* going with her – anywhere at all – was not an option.

We walked outside into an open meadow, into the faded glow from the waning moon, the forest a clotted darkness encircling everything.

"Any place in particular?" I asked, "or just into the night?"

She pointed across the field. "When I got here this afternoon, I saw a children's playground, over there I think. There was a jungle gym with a platform across the top. Let's go there. We can lie back and watch the meteors coming from Orion. And, I happen to have a joint of the best cannabis in Atlanta. You know, it's good for the heart."

Yes. Oh, hell yes.

We shared her joint. I followed her lead and stretched out on the plywood platform, but it became impossible for me to watch the meteor shower because there was no meteor shower. There was no Wicca gathering. There was no Lodge. There was nothing but this woman lying on her back beside me on the top of a kids' jungle gym in the middle of the Georgia mountains. I turned to look at her, again aware of an almost gravitational pull in her direction.

I knew I was high, the reefer had certainly done its job, but moving from one moment to the next was becoming extremely difficult. There was more at work here than *cannabis sativa*. Everything was happening at the same time. In the middle of it all I got the sense of being cut loose, the same feeling as when I was dancing with the three witches before the opening ceremony, untethered from that restrictive feeling of always being anchored, always held down, always tied by an unseen rope to the permanent now. But, that was gone. Was it Anita's presence that had set me loose? Was it her use of the Craft? A very small thought was trying to remind me that when something was cut loose it tended to float away and possibly disappear.

"How's this? Is this good?" she asked. I couldn't answer. She had turned and curled into me, resting an arm across my chest, her fingers sliding around to the back of my neck. "Is this comfortable for you?" she whispered. Comfortable? Yeah, let's use that word. I didn't want to say anything even remotely stupid.

We stayed on the platform for hours, I think. Hard to tell. But, it felt like timeless time, lying beside each other, breathing the same night air, hearing the same night creatures. Bliss. And, yes, I was feeling a mind-blowing sexual arousal that she must have been feeling also. But, all I could do was be aware of it; I couldn't respond to it. What would happen if I did? I mean, this woman was a witch. I had never been intimate with a witch. Too scary. And, besides, I didn't know any until the Grove. If the sex was unsatisfactory, then what? Would she change me into some sort of ugly creature? A frog? *A Conservative?* The possibility was too much even to consider.

The night went on and on. I've tried to recall exactly what happened, but all I have are questions. When did we leave the jungle-gym? Did we walk into the woods? What happened in that deeper darkness? Did I really hear the sounds I think I remember hearing, sounds that were coming from brilliant light that flashed from tree to tree, a freakish symphony of sighing and moaning and laughing? Was I terrified? Did I scream? I must have screamed. How long was I adrift in the forest with her? Did we talk? Did she have sex with me? Did she seduce me? And then erase all of it from my mind? I still don't know, can't recall.

The sounds and the lights and the rush of the ride through the forest, the impossibility of it all, began to fade. As it all receded, the echoes grew faint and then stopped altogether. A feeling of complete peace overtook me. I felt myself drifting down, down, down. I was falling into a bed. My bed. In the room I had taken in the Lodge. Sleep rolled over me. Muted colors and rounded shapes lulled me deeper and deeper into the comfort of whispering dreams.

And then, the sun.

The sun was flooding my room. I turned my face deeper into the pillow to escape the light. I wanted nothing, not the sun, not morning hunger, not the urge to get up to piss, nothing to disturb the profound sense of peace and balance I was feeling, something I had never before experienced.

There was a hesitant knock at the door. I hadn't ordered a wake-up call or room service. Again, a gentle knock. I rolled over on my back.

"Yeah . . .? What . . .? Who is it? No cleaning crew. Please come back later."

"I just wanted to say good-bye before I leave . . ." It was her. Bed to door, two seconds.

"Hi," I said, completely confused, trying to wake up, trying to process the good-bye. She set her back-pack on the hall floor and came into the room. The door whispered shut behind her.

"You're leaving? But, the conference just started. Last night. Why are you leaving?" The words were coming out way too fast, way too plaintive. "You're really leaving?"

"Yes. Believe me, if this hadn't come up I wouldn't go. Not after last night. My plan was to be here until Monday. But, a situation in Atlanta absolutely requires my being there."

"Is it serious? Must you go?"

"It's one of my patients. She had a serious set-back last night and is back in the ICU. They've been monitoring her, but her case is mine and I've got to get to the hospital as quickly as I can."

"You're a doctor?"

"Yes, a surgeon. Cardiology. My patient had a transplant last week. She was recovering nicely. Then this. My colleague called a few minutes ago. He thinks it's an embolism. That's the urgency."

I didn't know what to say. This was way beyond me. This was life and death. As was last night.

"You're a witch *and* a surgeon, too?"

"Yes. It's not as unusual as you might think."

From now on I knew I would question every doctor with whom I might have an appointment. *"Uh, no offense, doc, but are you a witch?"*

"Okay, I understand," I said. "Yeah, I do understand. You have to go."

"I hate leaving like this. Do you have something I can write on?"

I grabbed a note pad that had the Lodge's name embossed across the top and gave it to her.

"Here," she said. She tore off a page and handed it to me after writing something that brought the slightest smile to her face. Then she put her arms around me in a close embrace. I've done it so many times with so many people, a hug. This was way different.

"Uh . . . look . . . I . . ." I tried to come up with something timeless, like Rick, standing in the mist at the Casablanca airport saying good-bye to Ilsa, Captain Renault lurking nearby in the fog. Something like, *"We'll always have Paris."* Or, *"I'm no good at being noble, but it doesn't take much to see that the problems of three little people don't amount to a hill of beans in this crazy world . . ."* Of course, that would have made no sense at all. "I really want to see you again," was the best I could come up with.

She backed out of the room, her eyes locked with mine. The door shut, and I could hear her walk quickly away, through the Lodge's ornate, carved outer doors into the parking lot, and then silence.

Breakfast was available, but I decided to pass. No appetite. I was trying to sort out the events of last night, but it was difficult. Nothing that happened fit any model of reality I was familiar with and the entire night was fading, disappearing. Focus on the workshops, I told myself, and they were about to begin. I had signed up for two – as an observer only. The first was Wicca and Health. No, seriously. There are all sorts of ancient healing techniques that have been forgotten, lost in time, replaced by the pharmaceutical industry and its wretched chemicals. But the Olde Knowledge, the practices handed down from generation to generation of witches, the wisdom that got them condemned and tortured and burned alive for "defying God," was still in the old books and still available. All the herbs, potions, tinctures, and methods of preparing each healing agent was the subject of the workshop that was about to begin. I started walking across the meadow to the meeting room where the class would be conducted. It was a short distance, maybe seventy-five yards, but halfway across I felt a resistance with each step I took, as though I was moving through ankle-deep water. The feeling increased as I got closer to the jungle-gym, that, in the soft morning light with its metal tubes and vertical pipes, looked like a launch pad and, now that I considered it, it probably was. Last night's point of departure.

Maybe I had stumbled into a zone of dropped energy, some sort of psychic mud-puddle, possibly caused by a crowd of passing witches. In the context of everything that had happened in the past 18 hours, that was a real possibility. But, then, what *had* happened in those hours? I had no fucking idea. It was like looking into a kaleidoscope; lights, colors, pieces of reality suspended in ever-shifting patterns, but nothing coherent, nothing recognizable.

The Wicca and Health workshop started. The woman facilitating began by letting us know, "Witches do not smoke cigarettes. Witches do not get drunk. Witches *do* exercise. Witches *do* surround themselves with positive energy." And so on. Her lecture was not all that different from any healthy-living seminar. After listening for a few minutes, I stated to drift off. I tried to stay alert. I wanted to hear about the magic of herbs and fungi and woodsy things, but, I was tired, exhausted really. And, I was beginning to feel as though a valve, a stopcock had been left open and something was flowing out of me. I couldn't identify what it was. I didn't have the vocabulary. I decided to skip the rest of the workshop and go back to the Lodge for a quick nap. By the time I got to my room I felt an encompassing weakness. Something was wrong. The feeling of being emptied – that's the only way I know to put it – was not letting up. So, I did what the average person would do. I started to panic. I couldn't call 9-1-1. What would I say? I'm at a witches' convention and I have this weird feeling that I'm being emptied? Yeah, that would work. I left the room and walked to the main conference area. Surely, someone would be there who could help me figure out what the hell was happening. And, make it stop.

The woman who co-led the opening ceremony was sitting in the common area busy with a stack of papers. Last night's folding chairs had been collapsed and moved to the side of the room, replaced with several long tables piled with books,

Wicca magazines, charms, brochures, healing guides, candles, incense, silver jewelry, and a seeming endless supply of dried herbs neatly packaged in sealed plastic bags, a Wiccan *bodega*. She looked up as I approached.

"Hi. I'm sorry to interrupt, but I think I need a bit of help." I tried to keep it casual, but those little fingers of panic were drumming in my chest, making it hard to breathe.

"Oh, my," she said, looking at me with an expression of genuine concern. "You're leaking all over the place. I saw it when you started across the room."

Leaking? "Uh, what do you mean? I'm new here and I'm feeling weak, like something is flowing out of me. Not sure what to do." I then told her why I had come to this conference and that I was not a Wiccan. "So, can you help me? Did someone not see my purple badge and decide to cast a spell?"

She laughed. "No, no, no. This is a peaceful group. And we don't often cast spells like that. But, I see your aura is wide open and your *chi*, your energy, is flooding out of you, so something powerful happened to you. You wandered into something, for sure. Yes, I can help you. Don't panic. It's temporary and easy to fix. Here, sit." She pushed a chair toward me. I sat. She asked my name and told me hers: Locasta.

"Not sure what you mean, my '*aura. . .*'"

She reached out and took both my hands in hers. Immediately, the panicky feeling began to ease. "It's an energy field, a force field around each of us. If you know how to see it, it's there, about an inch outside and around our physical bodies. It acts as a shield of sorts. It protects us from the massive amounts of negativity that floods the planet. And that negativity is a killer. But, it appears your aura is wide open in several places and you look a bit like, well, a high-pressure hose with a bunch of holes in it." She chuckled when she said that. "Your energy, my dear, is shooting all over the room. Now, I want you to close your eyes and empty your mind. Can you do that?"

"I'll try."

It was easier than I thought. All the interior chatter, that endless stream of noise and images that moves like a swollen river every waking moment, started to get faint, drifting away from me.

"That's good," she said. "Now, focus on your breathing. Deep and peaceful. Deep and peaceful."

And, it was. I could hear only her voice and I began to feel a letting go so complete it was as though my cells were relaxing, which struck me as hysterically funny. I started laughing.

"Good!" she said. "That's good. Laughter's always good. How are you feeling now?"

"Not so panicky." Deep breath.

"Good! Your aura is beginning to close"

Deep breath.

"And, it's changing color, thank the Goddess! A crimson aura is not good. When you walked in here you looked like you were walking in a blast furnace. It's getting back to blue-green, now, which is where you want it, where it should be."

Deep breath.

She let go of my hands.

"Did you have some sort of disturbing thing happen to you recently? Dear Goddess, *something* left you full of holes."

"Yeah, well, it was intense . . ."

She chuckled again. "So, what happened?"

One more deep breath. I started to tell her about last night. I tried to find the words that would fully explain the impact Anita had on me, the hallucinogenic aspect of it all. She listened intently as I talked, staring at me as though she was surprised I was sitting there.

"Oh, my," she interrupted. "That was *you* with Anita?"

"Yes, and it was . . ."

"Well, to tell you the truth," she again interrupted, "I'm surprised you're still here. She must have decided to let you go free after she got whatever it was she wanted."

"What do you mean, 'Let me go free?' If I had wanted to, I could have walked away from her and I would have if I thought she was too weird. She wasn't. And, I don't think she took anything from me."

Again, she took my hands in hers, closing her fingers tightly, as if she was afraid I might float away.

"Well, maybe she didn't. But, you're not aware of who you were with last night. You have no idea, do you?"

I felt a slight twitch in my now almost-closed "aura," as if it was trying to open again.

"Anita," Locasta said softly, as if telling a secret, "as you call her, is a true sorceress. Her Wicca name is Circe. She has been around for a long time, and she has developed a power that seems to be boundless. To be honest, most witches are a bit afraid of her. She has quite the temperament. But, we do respect her knowledge and I'm sure some of us envy it. Occasionally, she'll show up at one of the conferences, we assume to simply participate and have fun, and perhaps meet privately with any of us who might want to learn from her. Most often, no one does. Our little paradox is that some of the knowledge contained in the Craft requires a great deal of study and spiritual balance before it can be shared. Most witches don't try to reach that level, not anymore. That deep knowledge so often seems to bring conflict. And those of us who have talked with her get the feeling that she may wish she could rid herself of what she has learned."

"But, I thought deep knowledge was an important part of Wicca, of the Craft."

"And, it surely is," Locasta said, "but, so much of that knowledge was necessary back in the dark times, the Dark Ages. The survival of a few of us depended on that knowledge, especially given how many of us were burned, drowned, hunted down by Mastiffs and torn to pieces." As she talked, she continued to shuffle her papers, occasionally marking a section with yellow high-lighter. She didn't seem disturbed in the least in telling me that her forebears had been burned, drowned, and disemboweled.

"But, now, it's risky to get into all that strange wisdom. The knowledge is useless, it can't be applied given the dissonance that seems to be everywhere you look. It could only be used for destruction. A cleansing destruction perhaps, but destruction nonetheless."

I got what she was saying about how fucked up everything seemed to be. It was part of my profession, to pick apart all the ugly shit that was so toxic, so destructive to even the idea, the thought, of peace or justice, which seemed to be concepts that no longer applied.

Locasta laid the hi-lighter on the table, stood up and walked around behind me. "We're almost finished," she said. "One last bit and you're good as new." Reaching around, she placed one hand on my forehead and the other in the center of my chest. She repeated a few words that sounded like *Ly O Lay Ale Loya, Ly O Lay Ale Loya, Ly O Lay Ale Loya* and then slowly let her hands drop to her sides. And, that was that.

"All better?" she asked. "Everything closed and secure?"

It was. "Thank you so much, Locasta. A few minutes ago, I felt like I was going to explode. You fixed me."

"Happy to do it. Now, go and sin no more." We both laughed.

I went back to my room and started tossing things into my duffel bag. There was no reason to stay any longer. That day's workshops were ending and I damn sure was not going to participate in the evening's Waning Moon Festival, whatever that was. Not after my experience with Anita. At this point, I realized I was in territory I had no business being in. Maybe back in Atlanta getting together with Anita would be manageable, less surreal. I reached into my pocket and pulled out the piece of paper on which she had written, I assumed, her phone number. It was blank except for a quickly drawn pentagram above the name *Circe*. Of course. What did I expect?

As I pulled out of the Lodge parking lot I started laughing.

Chapter 21

Leaving Atlanta

The pressure from the religious kooks who didn't like my on-air point of view about their anti-everything-but-Jesus bullshit was becoming more than just a comedic irritation. The warnings left on my voice-mail were coming almost daily; the usual death threats, promises to burn down my house, imprecatory prayers that would consign my immortal soul to immortal horror, the sort of pain and suffering that can only be conjured in the fevered brains of religious True Believers. All that nonsense about "God's love" and "Peace on Earth" and salvation and redemption and forgiveness was washed away in a flood of ugliness that is always the subtext of religion. After all, the secondary function of organized religion is to teach us who to hate, who to condemn, who to find utterly unworthy of life itself. The primary function is to ease our terrifying fear of death, and all of it is the product of primitive Stone Age minds.

Apparently, two calls to WSB threatening total destruction was sufficient to get some advice as to what to do, how to protect myself. Lt. Frazier was interested in what I had to tell him without showing the usual skepticism that accompanies phoned-in threats that promise to turn someone into red mist and bone fragments. Domestic terrorism has always been on the radar of law enforcement, especially in the South given the region's history of lynchings, bombings, race hatred, religious bigotry, and all the other violence that has been directed at those not considered fully human by the white Christians who decide who the current and future targets will be.

It's the mid-80s and the white supremacists and religious psychos, together with whacked-out groups calling themselves, "Sons of Confederate Veterans," and "The League of the South," along with that ol' stand-by here in Dixie, the Ku Klux Klan and its newly minted militia gangs made up of astonishingly ignorant, ugly as hell middle-age white men determined to protect racial "purity," are all experiencing a terrifying realization that has somehow penetrated their collective cerebrums, a sudden understanding that the so-called "white race" is heading toward minority status as a result of demographics and the die-off of red-necks who just don't believe the constant use of drugs and alcohol along with a diet of peanut-butter and bacon omelets and mayonnaise-saturated stewed tomato and pork-chop sandwiches on white bread so you have to lift and eat quick lest it fall through the crust, are really, really bad for your health. Taken together, this collection of knuckle-draggers provides local law enforcement with lots to do. There's always some pickup-truck-load of screaming, beer-drinking, Confederate flag waving morons, most of whom seem to have learned to walk upright just that morning who believe a critical component of their manhood requires walking into their local Wal-Mart with an AR-15 casually draped over a shoulder, cuz the 2nd Amendment says they can. So, Lt. Frazier and I had our serious heart-to-heart, or about as close to that as you can come with an expert on domestic terrorism. As a result of that conversation, I was now the owner of a Glock 9 and a Georgia concealed-carry permit.

Some of the right-wing kooks who tuned in to my program did so "to see what the other side's saying." They truly believe liberals are aliens sent here from somewhere far away – possibly released through some Hell Gate - to disrupt the natural order of things and, therefore, must be stopped. The wing-nuts' political and religious points-of-view never vary, no matter what part of the country they live in. Abortion? *Verboten.* Not because of their insistence that being anti-abortion is being "pro-life." No, so-called pro-life is just the marketing part, the midway barker shouting for the rubes to step inside to see the creature that is half-lizard, half-man, the only one in captivity! The truth is this: The right-wing, evangelical, religio-fascist, authoritarian, sub-culture in this "Christian" nation cannot allow women – the fountainhead of all grief and lamentations because they are the ones who introduced the human species to DEATH – to assert authority of any type or to any degree over men. Paul in his letters to the early Church in Corinth, insisted that women were to remain silent during services. The leaders (chosen by God) were men only. No singing for the girls, no audible prayer, no preaching, nothing. Just sit there and shut the fuck up, ladies. You had your chance six thousand years ago at the creation and you blew it, big time. And, God is punishing you with painful childbirth, a curse which is beyond insanely silly now, what with epidurals and Percocet. And birth control pills (more accurately, pregnancy control pills) allow women to do what men have done since forever: Have as much sexual freedom as a gal can handle, which drives the fundamentalist males who follow any one of the Abrahamic religions abso-fucking-lutely crazy. According to "scripture," women are to be subordinate to men; men are the leaders, both in the family and in the nation, even though the fellas have shown an incredible lack of ability to do either, instead causing war, famine, death, disaster, and eventually, one presumes, annihilation of the human species. Politically, it's even worse. When you consider the lies, deceptions, posturings, and the sundry horseshit male candidates use to convince the perpetually stupid to vote them into office, you have to wonder how the human species made it this far up the tree of evolution without becoming extinct.

Thus, these right-wing crazies decided my brand of political talk as not only affecting the ladies in an unacceptable way, but also might be working its way into the still malleable thinking processes of the kids. The crazies knew that exposing the youth of America – certainly of Atlanta - to politically progressive ideas would lead to all sorts of undesirable shit. Like, drug use, and atheism, and wild, monkey-sex with god knows who when Mom and Dad weren't paying attention; and shoplifting and deciding religious nuttery was not needed in their young life plans. In other words, the young people of Atlanta were being exposed to lefty, Communist, godless, anarchy. And, the good, patriotic Christians whose responsibility was to protect the young from such liberal bullshit was not going to allow this to continue. Getting me off the air became yet one more obsession for Atlanta's guardians of morality and order. After all, by god, there is no First Amendment protection of speech anywhere in the Bible.

One rainy Fall morning I was called into the Program Director's office for yet another bullshit session on *a)* why did

I persist in the liberal crap, and b) what was WSB going to do with me? The answer to (b) had already been decided. I knew there was trouble afoot when I walked into Greg's office and there sat not just Greg, but also the HR woman, the General Manager, and the station's attorney.

Greg went first: "So, Mike, how's it going?" Actually, not bad and Greg knew it. I had great Arbitron numbers, and an expanding audience which was a major problem for the station, not to mention a huge embarrassment. The ratings numbers' upward trend was coming from demographics not considered to be the most desirable audience the station wanted, and the sales department was reluctant to mention this to potential advertisers. The demographics were young people, students, non-whites, former radicals, urban professionals, a population that was slowly becoming a huge chunk of the Atlanta market and one my mis-guided bosses wanted to avoid as long as possible. The sought-after audience was, instead, white, Conservative, Christian and mostly male, the theory being that while it was women who made the family spending decisions, the husbands had veto power. The Bible says that is the way God ordered it, according to the fundamentalist church leaders who teach the faithful about fear, obedience, subservience, and all the other bloody lies that have been the core of the Abrahamic religions since, well, since Abraham.

Then, adopting a tone of voice similar to that of a concerned parent who knows his four-year-old hates broccoli, Greg said, "You don't seem very happy here, lately. The police are coming by on a regular basis, we're getting all sorts of threats. The managers are getting awkward questions when they go to church . . ."

"Uh, Greg, those are not my problems. In fact, I'm real

goddam happy being here at the Voice of the South! I can't stop the wing-nuts from getting all frothed up because I threaten their bullshit." But, I knew the jig was just about up. "I'm having a total ball being the voice of the anti-Christ every night. Why, is someone complaining?"

The HR lady piped up, her face slightly flushed: "Mike, I have a check here for you in the amount of 10-thousand dollars . . ."

"Oh, my, you're paying me a *bonus?* Why, that's swell!!"

Then the General Manager weighed in: "Seriously, Mike, we're going to sign with Dr. Laura, and she does her syndicated show the same day part you're on the air. The check is severance pay. So . . ."

"Dr. Laura??!!" I almost shouted. "Are you fucking kidding me? The woman is a physiologist who wants people to think she's a therapist! She's a fraud, folks. And she poses nude, her legs all spread open like an invitation! Your supposed audience is going to appreciate *that?* What about the kiddies?!"

The corporate attorney finally opened up: "Now, hold on, Mike. She's as professional as you are. She's credentialed, unlike you, and I don't think it's a good idea calling her a fraud. Certainly not in front of witnesses."

Witnesses? My soon-to-be-former co-workers were now witnesses?! And, I got the zinger about credentials. Asshole.

My turn: "Okay, you all are sounding like a firing squad that's trying to pretend you're loaded with blanks. So, what's the bottom line here, gang? Do I get a last cigarette? A blindfold?"

HR lady: "Now, Mike, it's not like that at all. Times are changing, and the political climate is drifting to the right. We just want you to be in an environment where you're happy, where your particular message will resonate."

Resonate? What the fuck was my "message" doing if not "resonating?" Wasn't that why this bullshit meeting was taking place to begin with? I was probably the most resonating talk show host in the South, only on all the wrong points-of-view according to these clowns who were about to broom me.

"So, what we have here," HR lady continued, "is a solution to all our problems; yours, the station's and our core listeners." Honest to god I thought she was going to say what we have here is a failure to communicate, like the sadistic warden in *Cool Hand Luke*. The only failure involved management's cowardice. Their daily broadcast line-up was loaded with right-wing talkers who spewed half-truths, misstatements, deceptions, and full-on lies. The Rush Limbaugh model had swallowed talk radio, coast to coast and border to border, across the fruited plane, just as the bloated idiot claimed. But, I wanted to hear HR lady's "solution."

"We want to give you this check as severance pay and provide you with a sterling recommendation signed by the president of the company. You know, WSB is known nationwide and this kind of recommendation will go a long way in helping you find a position at another radio station here in Atlanta, or a different market altogether. You know, there are thousands of stations across the country."

What she was leaving out, of course, was the absolute lack of any commercial radio station in the Atlanta market that presented any political talk other than the right-wing bullshit that was sinking the entire country into a sea of neo-fascist madness. So, if continuing in the business of resisting the rising flood of American fascism was in my future, it would not be in Atlanta.

"You're serious, right Greg?" I said to my soon-to-be ex-boss. "Laura Fucking Schlesinger? I will admit she's unique. A so-called therapist who advocates emotional brutality. Jesus, is that the best you can do?" Oops. This time the "F" word snapped their heads around. "We don't think crass language is called for in this discussion, Mike. And there is a lady present," Greg said, nodding in the direction of the HR woman who rolled her eyes at the demeaning, and phony, male concern for her tender ears. She laid the check on Greg's desk and said, "I've got some paper work to attend to, so if you gentlemen will excuse me . . ." And, out the door she went. Greg got on the office intercom and asked Security to report to his office. I was going to get an honest-to-god escort off the property. The company attorney said he had a luncheon meeting and scurried away. The GM looked at me, shook his head, and started to say something. He immediately stopped himself after one syllable that sounded like "gack." He followed the attorney down the hall.

"Here's your severance check," Greg said as he handed me the envelope the HR woman had left. I took it and followed the GM and the attorney out the door. Waiting for me in the hall was one of the rent-a-cops the station had salted through the property to scare off any homeless person who might want to sit in the shade of one of the huge oaks that sheltered the station's vast front lawn, a stretch of green that sloped down to traffic-choked Peachtree Street. Of course, a homeless person on this manicured lawn was not going to happen. The sight of a warped grocery cart loaded with some wretched person's entire life framed by the ante-bellum-style building as a backdrop, was not a scene station management wanted as daily rush hour traffic crept by.

The rent-a-cop, Jesse, was surprised to see who he had to escort off the property. "You, man? You? The only liberal on the station? What the fuck happened? They catch you with the manager's wife? Damn! Who we going to listen to now? Those threats you were getting must have gotten to the bosses, right? Shit, man, what you gonna do?"

"I have no idea, Jesse. I'll just get the word out that I'm looking for a new gig, I guess. Maybe put a 'situation wanted' ad in Broadcast Magazine. Something will turn up." Yeah, for sure.

Chapter 22

The Rock

About fifteen miles east of Atlanta, a mountain of granite looms over the surrounding countryside. It is 1600 feet tall and a mile and a half wide. A path around the base covers five miles. On the northern face of the mountain is a massive bas-relief carving of three men who, in the mid-19th century, committed treason against the United States that resulted in the deaths of 700-thousand Americans. Depicted in granite are the three leaders of the Confederacy: Robert E. Lee, Stonewall Jackson, and Jefferson Davis. This glorious memorial to treason and death was begun by the sculptor Gutzon Borglum, the same man who carved the iconic figures staring into nothingness on Mt. Rushmore.

Borglum was a nativist who was approached in 1915 by one of the leaders of The United Daughters of the Confederacy – Helen Plane. The ladies wanted a monument that would commemorate the heroes who attempted to destroy the United States, an effort that left, in addition to the acres of dead, tens of thousands more who were maimed and starved and tortured. These traitors deserved a monument? Okay, but more appropriately on a mountain in Hell. However, Hell being a religious construct that does not exist, Stone Mountain would serve as a substitute. When he accepted the project, Borglum agreed to include a KKK altar at the top of the mountain. The demand from Ms. Plane came with a note that read, almost incoherently, "I feel it is due to the KKK that saved us from Negro domination and carpetbag rule and that it be memorialized on Stone Mountain." (sic) The same year Borglum agreed to the project, the Klan was re-born on the top of the mountain with all the pageantry for which the Klan had become famous: White men roaming around in their pointy-headed sheets, their rat-like eyes peering through holes as they watched dozens of flaming crosses – a symbol of their beloved heavenly Savior – burning hate into the night. Speeches were made by craven, semi-literate creatures whose insides were being slowly corroded by the acidic hatred that had already liquified and destroyed their dark souls. The resurrection ceremony presented the sort of weird, insane terror designed to instill further fear and panic in the black population. To the white citizens of the Jim Crow South it was all glorious, a celebration of the way things were when their world made sense, when black folk could be owned, beaten, raped, skinned, boiled, all because the psychotic God of the white folks had ordained this to be the fate of the dark-skinned African natives whose greatest misfortune was being born.

Borglum, at some point, must have realized what he had become a part of. He abruptly abandoned the project in 1925, fled Georgia, and went to work on Mt. Rushmore. It was reported that for the rest of his life he was unable to sleep on white sheets.

The state of Georgia bought the mountain in 1958 as a

tribute to the hundreds of thousands of Southerners who died defending the "Lost Cause": slavery. The racist, murderous carving was finished in 1972. Stone Mountain Park itself was opened to the public on April 14, 1965, 100 years to the day after the assassination of Abraham Lincoln, a claw in the eye to all those race-mixing, mongrelizing Yankees who so openly defied God's law.

I had climbed this strange mountain numerous times, usually timing the climb so I'd reach the summit as the sun set behind the Atlanta skyline to the west. The silence on the mountain at dusk was profound. Red-tailed hawks swooped silently through the fading light, eventually disappearing into the pine forests that covered the lower elevations. Mist from the valley below slowly crept up the rocky incline trying in vain to reach the summit. Ghosts moved brazenly around the mountain sliding in and out of the forest, dancing over the rocks and boulders, leaving a momentary trail of shimmering ectoplasm that faded as quickly as it appeared. Altogether, it was a visual symphony of night mysteries and haunting visitors.

This had become my place to think, to feel as though I was literally above the issues and problems that insisted on attention, that demanded to be solved, that were, possibly, making me crazy, like having to waste time dodging the religious nut-balls who would have been very comfortable conducting another Inquisition, because, as I'm sure they would agree, another one was long overdue.

After the long climb to the top, I fired up a joint and leaned back into one of the concave granite boulders that were scattered about. I needed a plan, something that would get me away from thinking about the Christian madness and the political fascism that was beginning to engulf the country. Finally, I fell asleep, lulled into peaceful oblivion by the star-spangled darkness and the whispery breezes chasing the ghosts around the contours of the mountain. The tapping of raindrops woke me up. I glanced at my watch as I moved to the near-by shelter of a tight grove of stunted pine trees. Three o'clock in the morning. The park gates had been closed and locked four hours ago. I hoped the park police would assume my car was left in the parking lot at the bottom of the mountain due to some sort of mechanical trouble and would be retrieved when the sun came up and the park re-opened. The rain now had me wide awake. No more sleep tonight. I found a spot under the trees that provided a cover that would keep me dry. The rain continued, increasing in intensity and bringing with it a sense of sadness and loss that started to settle over me. It was the mountain. I remembered a couple of lines from a poem written by a friend years ago: *"You're closer now, closer, just one step above, mountains for thinking and valleys for love . . ."* I had to focus on something pleasant while the rain splattered around me, something that might take me to one of those valleys.

The park gates would open at 8 AM, which meant I could get off the mountain and away from this open-air Confederate mausoleum in about an hour. It's not that I didn't enjoy the climb up Stone Mountain and the incredible view of the surrounding countryside once at the peak. I did. And, frequently. But, falling asleep on this huge granite rupture in Atlanta's suburban landscape left me stiff and sore and wet from the night's steady rain, as though that was the price of missing the park's closing time and spending the night where spending the night was not allowed. The park was littered with signs warning overnight camping was allowed in designated campsites only, and the top of the mountain was not one of them. To make a bad situation worse, there was that fucking carving, too. Sleeping that close to images of the traitors responsible for so much death gave me a cold feeling inside that couldn't be eased. Or maybe, it was just the rain.

But, I got what I was seeking. A possible solution to the ennui that was starting to choke me. I wanted to stay in talk radio, but it sure wasn't going to happen in Atlanta. My now shit-canned contract with WSB had contained a "no-compete" clause, a nasty little device radio station managers use to prevent a popular on-air personality in talk, rock, jazz, whatever, from changing stations within a given market and taking thousands of listeners away from the station that no longer wanted him (or, eventually, her) and moving those listeners to the new station. That section of my agreement with WSB was the part Ms. Human Resource lady had totally ignored when she suggested another Atlanta radio gig as I was being fired. So, since radio work in Atlanta was out of the question for me, it was time to leave.

As an added impetus to get the hell out of Dixie, I knew I needed a break from the South and the red-neck bullshit that seemed to underlie everything about this part of the country. For many reasons, some esthetic, some cultural, I had come to love Atlanta, arguably the region's capitol. But, I'd gotten so sick of seeing Confederate monuments, obelisks, carvings, memorials, and cemeteries throughout the South. Why were they there to begin with? Why wasn't every commemoration of these American traitors long ago removed from public property? Could statues of Nazi "heroes" be found in the public parks of Germany? Were there granite memorials to the Vichy French in Paris? On the other hand, I was okay with the cemeteries. They could stay. They were cold reminders of the actual cost of the hellish destruction the slave-owing, wealthy, American upper class of the mid-19th century had brought to the ignorant, poor, white militias whose blood saturated the loamy soil of Virginia, seeped into the red clay of Georgia, soaked the black dirt of Mississippi and the sandy grit of southern Alabama, and all of it in order to keep the white slave-owners in positions of absolute power. The beautiful, pastoral South? Blood-soaked. Every square inch of it. And all this death and destruction was supposed to represent Southern honor and nobility and Christian values? There was no honor in the so-called "Lost Cause," none. The equestrian monuments and heroically posed statues dedicated to Southern generals in their acts of treason, represented lies, illusions, and shameful attempts to rationalize two-hundred and fifty years of subjecting other human beings to unspeakable horror, terror, and the denial of their humanity. And that warrants celebration? Only if you are out of your fucking mind.

Chapter 23

Chicago

A few months into my forced unemployment, the Program Director at WLS in Chicago answered a "situation wanted" ad I had placed in a radio industry magazine. He asked for an audition tape and a resume, which I put in the mail the next day. Within a week, he called.

"I liked your tape," he said, a hint of relief in his voice. PDs were swamped with unrequested audition tapes, more often than not sent by one more small market, right-wing moron who was absolutely convinced he was destined to be the next Rush Limbaugh, if he could just escape his afternoon drive gig in Broken Elbow, Missouri. That is, as soon as Limbaugh choked to death on his own bile while screaming to his audience that the "Liberals" were vermin, scum, the worst of the worst, and they were destroying everything, and the only thing that would stop them would be their disappearance from the face of the earth, one way or another. Or maybe his demise would be caused by his massive opioid habit.

El Rushbo's pill popping was getting out of hand. No longer able to find a doctor in South Florida who willing to write, honest, doc, just one more prescription, the Dean of The Institute of Advanced Conservative Studies turned to his housekeeper. He sent her into the streets to find dealers who would provide her with handfuls of Oxycontin she could deliver to the Dean and thus keep her job cleaning his bathrooms and scrubbing his floors. It was a workable arrangement for a while. She got 'em, he swallowed 'em. Until he was arrested for "doctor shopping." By then he had driven himself deaf from drug use, he was gobbling Oxy's at the rate of 3,000 in six months and, according to published reports at the time, told the court it was all because of his "back pain." This ridiculous excuse was coming from the Conservative icon who had raged against drug users in general and mocked Bill Clinton who stupidly said he smoked reefer when he was younger but didn't inhale. After intense meetings with several Florida prosecutors, Limbaugh's top-seeded lawyers worked a deal with the authorities, a deal unavailable to the common folk busted on the same charges. All el-Rushbo had to do was complete a rehab program (that included a literal "pat the pony" exercise that Limbaugh found so therapeutic) and promise never, never to do those nasty drugs again, and he was home free. The charges would be dismissed, and all would be forgiven and forgotten, although this law-and-order hypocrite had repeatedly made the case on his radio show that drug crimes deserve punishment. Another ironic point Limbaugh made was that statistics showed Blacks go to prison more often than whites for the same drug offense, which, to Mr. Conservative meant "too many whites are getting away with drug use." And, all this was said righteously and unctuously while he was getting away with drug use. Un-fucking-real.

"I liked your tape because you obviously know what you're

talking about," the Chicago PD continued, "and, your liberal stance on issues. That's unusual. I've got boxes of audio tapes stacked in my office from creepy, weird sounding characters who try to convince me they deserve a slot on WLS. Funny stuff. So, since I liked your tape, I'd like to hear more. Can you come to Chicago for an interview?"

"I'm halfway there."

Carl Sandburg nailed it. "Chicago" is Chicago.

I spent the next three years in the country's third largest market working at a station owned and operated by the ABC radio network, which was, in turn, owned by the Disney Corp. I knew from day one this would be a short-lived affair. Me? With Disney? The nation's preeminent family-focused entertainment behemoth? The thought of this relationship coming to anything other than a bad end was easily dismissed. The city itself was both an incubator and reservoir of the best of American culture from theater to architecture, design to couture, visual art to authors, poets, and musicians to the point of being pleasantly overwhelming.

It also was a deep pool of racial violence and gang murders unabated since Capone. The week I arrived a black teenager was beaten to death by a mob of whites armed with baseball bats and tire irons because he inadvertently wandered into the Bridgeport neighborhood, an enclave of white ethnic families that could easily have been transplanted from 1970s South Africa. The violence of the attack on this kid was stupefying. It was the same level of sadism as anything found in the stereotyped South and it was a horrific reminder that racism in America was not bound within a specific region of the country. There were all sorts of targets for the madness of white racism and Christian bigotry: African-Americans; Native Americans;

Latinos; homosexual men and women; recent immigrants who had yet to assimilate into a culture that looked on the new arrivals with suspicion often followed by violence; Muslims; Jews; atheists; the list was, and is, endless.

My first week at WLS was a get-to-know-you process with a new audience, one not all that different from what I had left behind in Atlanta. I took a call the first or second night from a guy who wanted to know – right now! - my position on guns and the Second Amendment. There was no way, apparently, I could get away from these assholes. "I'm armed and dangerous," I said to the caller. That seemed to satisfy him.

"Well, I'm glad you're not one of these gun-grabbing liberals who are trying to take away the only protection we've got anymore." I decided to poke the bear: "Protection from what? What are you afraid of? Is there someone out to get you? Mafia looking for you?"

"C'mon, you know who's causing all the trouble in this city. You read the papers. They won't stay in their own areas and they come over here looking to rob and rape and steal anything they can get their hands on. By god, if they come to my house I'll shoot first and ask questions after they're dead and they can't answer! Ha-ha-ha-ha!" That was some funny shit to this caller – asking questions after they're dead. Yuk-yuk.

The next night a cop called in from his patrol car, he said. That was a first.

"So, I heard you say last night you own a gun, is that right?"

"That's correct, officer. I do. It's a 9mm Glock with a 15-plus-1 capacity. Learned to shoot it at a police practice range in Atlanta."

"Well, I hate to tell you this, but you're in violation of the law here in Chicago. You better get rid of it."

"But, I have a permit to carry it."

"Not here in Chicago, you don't."

"Get rid of it? Do you know how much it cost? Several hundred dollars."

"Then break it down and put the parts away. You can't legally own a gun in Chicagoland." Irony. It was inescapable. Chicago had countless shootings and multiple deaths every weekend and yet it was a crime to own a hand gun.

My on-air shift at WLS was from 10PM until 1AM, the same as it was in Atlanta. I liked working at night, especially in talk radio, even though it had become talk radio's liberal ghetto in just about every market in the country if, that is, the station had a liberal on-air personality. The various owners were convinced advertisers would leave in droves if, god forbid, a liberal voice could be heard during the day talking about issues from an honest and factual point of view instead of the lunatic conspiracy theories and outright lies dumped into the airwaves by the cadre of right-wing rabble-rousers who, by design, were flooding the radio broadcast spectrum. Were those owners correct? Did corporate America want only right-wing or neo-Fascist views broadcast around their products and services? As long as no one identified it as such, yes.

An entirely different sort of person tuned in at night: Insomniacs, college student, retirees, over-the-road truckers, conspiracy nuts, radical right-wingers, radical left-wingers, sex workers ending another miserable night walking Michigan Avenue, the city's "Magnificent Mile," and the occasional schizophrenic who wanted to let me know (and anyone listening across 30 States and parts of Canada) about the flood of spindly aliens moving into a deep ravine behind his house. Or the guy one night who insisted his dog was breaking into pieces and he didn't know who to call and could I please, please help. After a few disjointed bits of semi-hysterical conversation, it became apparent to me his dog was having puppies but explaining that to him was impossible. "No! He's not having puppies! He's a boy! Boys don't have puppies, you stupid! He's breaking into pieces!" The night was filled with madness and I absolutely wanted my share of it. The crazy in Chicago was so different from the crazy in the South. Southerners, both black and white, kept the relatives who were deep in a different reality away from the general population and referred to them as "funny."

"Auntie Clarice is sorta funny, you know what I'm saying?" was all that was necessary to let a visitor know Aunt Clarice was out of her fucking mind and might pick up a carving knife at any moment, with any provocation, and start stabbing things. "Funny" had an entirely different meaning in the South when applied to the relatives. Southern families made sure Uncle Crazy stayed in the attic. He had a nice, cozy corner with a comfortable mattress and a radio (his magic "talking box") where he could chat with his night visitors – the ones who lived in the closet - any time he wanted to, if he kept them from screaming, which some of them were inclined to do. Auntie Clarice could roam the house as she wanted provided some other family member was home, and if she promised not to unlock the front door or any of the windows to let in the people who were making faces at her outside on the lawn. Dementia was handled differently, of course. It was much quieter and orderly, and that was especially important when it was time for Wednesday night prayer services at church. Speaking in "tongues" is one thing, and entirely appropriate for religious nuts, but allowing slowly disappearing Grandma to offer her version of this fundamentalist bullshit? No way. The risks of having God talk using Grandma's vocal chords far outweighed the benefits. Northern crazy, on the other hand, was demonstrative. Loud. Insistent. And so much of it took place on the street, occasionally near a pay phone where a call could be made to my program to tell me about disintegrating dogs.

After a few months of this, I realized I had to respond in a way that wasn't overtly mocking. That's when I came up with "Pocket Puppies." On the air one night I made up a ridiculous story about a discovery in Australia. Using genetic manipulation, it was now possible to produce little dogs no larger than a six-pack of Post-Its. And, they didn't bark. They made little beeping sounds, like a dump-truck backing up. I thought listeners might hesitate for a moment and then realize it was all bullshit. Surprise! People started calling in and asking my producer where they could get their own Pocket Puppy. I had to pause whatever topic I had moved on to and explain I was just kidding. Pocket puppies didn't exist. Even after I made that clear, callers still wanted one and got pissed off when I finally convinced them it was all a joke.

Just for shits and giggles, I decided to do fuck with their minds again a few nights later. Only this time I'd make it a little more believable, a little closer to what the city of Chicago might really try to do since issuing parking tickets or towing away a hapless driver's car parked at an expired meter in the heart of downtown, or in a space where the language on the parking signs was indecipherable English, seemed to be the *raison d'etre* for the city's traffic division. I waited until a Friday night's program. City offices would be closed for the weekend giving listeners two days to freak out, and by Monday, there would be an avalanche of calls to various municipal offices wanting to know who's fucked-up idea this was. On the designated Friday night, near the end of the program, I said the city was about to come up with a new revenue-raising scheme: Walking Permits. They were to be issued by the police department and one would be necessary if residents wanted to walk in downtown Chicago. The sticker cost would start at $15 a year and would increase depending on the weight of the buyer. Up to 150 pounds, $15; 150 to 200 pounds, $25; over 250 pounds, $50. Kids under 12 would get a free sticker. If your first sticker cost $25 and you lost weight you could request a review and get a less costly permit. And vice-versa, of course. And, I added, there was the additional benefit of an incentive to lose a bit of weight. I said I had noticed an abundance of overweight people in this "hog butcher for the world" city and I believed this could be Chicago's way of helping them get healthy. The sticker had to be displayed when walking the city's streets; stuck on a briefcase would do, or a hip pocket, a jacket lapel, somewhere easily visible from the street so a cop in a cruising police car could see it. The first offense of not having sticker would be a $25 fine. The second offense would increase the fine to $100. Third offense? The illegal pedestrian would be barred from walking in a forty-block square in the middle of Chicago – unless it was to keep a doctor's appointment – for a year. My producer played the show's closing theme and I said good night.

Much to my delight, all hell broke loose Saturday morning. There were a few people catching up on clerical work at City Hall and they were inundated with calls, all of which followed a general theme: "Are you people crazy? Has Mayor Daley lost his mind? Walking permits??! No fucking way!" And, like that. All day Saturday.

Early Monday morning, around 7:00 AM, the Program Director called me at home. He sounded a bit concerned.

"How quick can you get down here? We need to talk."

"Well, I just woke up, boss. Gimme an hour?"

"Make it less than that." Click.

I had the feeling he was pissed off about something. He was a fairly intense person (he said it was because of his time in Vietnam) so I knew it could be anything. While I showered and dressed I tried to think what I might have done to get him angry. I couldn't come up with anything.

I got off the el, walked into ABC's broadcast building, took the elevator to the eighth floor, down the hall and into his office. He kept his eyes on whatever he was doing, writing shit, checking off numbers, until he finally motioned to the chairs facing his desk and said, "Sit down." Not good. No hello or how was your weekend or anybody die recently in your family? Nothing but, 'sit down.'

After a couple of very quiet minuets and a lot of writing he looked up.

"So, what the hell did you say on the air Friday night?"

"About what? I covered a bunch of topics. Which one?"

"The one where you apparently said the city was going to issue walking permits! *Walking permits?!* Are you crazy? People fucking believed you! This is Chicago, for Chrissake! People know that kind of shit is possible! No, probable! Daley's office called here an hour ago, 6:00 AM for fuck's sake, really, really pissed off at the station! Do you know how many calls they got Saturday? How many messages were left Sunday? How many calls they got starting at 5:00 AM today?"

"Well, no. How many?"

"*How many . . .?!*"

"Yeah, you said did I know how many calls? So, I'm just answering you. How many? I'm really curious."

"The actual number's immaterial! It doesn't matter! The mayor's office called here, and they were furious! Daley doesn't like the kind of attention your little comedy bit got him. He's dealing with that whole Dad thing, trying to live up to his old man's reputation and your making people think he's going to issue walking stickers doesn't help. Jesus, where did you come up with that? Why'd you come up with that?"

"Just made it up. I thought people would get a laugh out of it."

"Okay, well, tonight you're gonna *un-make* it up. And, don't do this kind of shit again, seriously. You're on the air in a city that has a long history with radio. People here tend to believe what they hear. They don't know you from Adam's house-cat, but they give you a lot of credibility simply because you are on the radio. You say walking stickers are going to be required and people believe you." He went on and on about the responsibilities of a broadcaster, and the reputation of a "heritage" station like WLS and then into corporate identity and its importance, and the fragility of a station's broadcast license if the right-wing nut cases decided to file FCC challenges to a station's license renewal. After twenty minutes of this gibberish I wanted to ram pencils into my ears so I couldn't hear any more managerial whining. Finally, mercifully, he ran out of ways to give me more hell and stopped. After a bit of respectful silence, I told him I got what he was saying and apologized for freaking out city hall. And him. But, the message I really got was there were too many assholes in Chicago who couldn't tell the difference between a joke and reality. And this was the home of the Second City comedy troupe? Come to think of it, how could people appreciate parody when the President of the United States was discovered getting blowjobs from a White House intern and then committing perjury thinking, crazily, that he could hide it all. The truth is, reality, especially political reality, tends to shred parody, to reduce it to rubble.

I took the el home from WLS late one night – early morning, 3 AM – after joining some of the station staff at a co-worker's birthday party at a downtown pub. I walked from my stop through the deserted streets of the neighborhood, Rogers Park. Years before, it had been a predominantly working-class Jewish community; now, it was the home turf of violent Jamaican drug gangs, or so I had been warned, which left me a little jumpy. Chicago is known as a city of extreme gun violence and I didn't want to walk into a spray of bullets on their way from an AK-47 to a rival drug dealer's torso. To avoid even the possibility of that happening, I turned off the main drag and into the alley that would take me to the rear of my four-unit apartment building. I opened the gate, walked in to the yard and sensed movement in the darkness near the garage, which was barely big enough to provide one precious parking space per apartment. I stopped walking and looked towards the movement. A person was standing in the corner. Oh, shit. I'm gonna be killed.

"Yo! You in the corner. Why are you in my yard?" I said, my voice trembly, which was a weak-ass question to ask when I was only moments away from dying and becoming one more Chicago corpse.

"Aw, man, ain't doin' shit. Just walkin' through off Sheridan, just cuttin' through your yard. No big deal, man." He stepped into the hazy light from the bare light fixture on the corner of the garage. "No trouble, man, just cuttin' through. You live here?" he asked, as if we were about to become big time friends and he wanted to get a fix on where our relationship had its beginning.

"Yeah, I live here, and you don't, right?" I answered his question with a question of my own, sounding a lot ballsier than I intended.

"Chill, man. I ain't lookin' for trouble." He started to move past me toward the still open back gate. "See? I'm outta here already. Everything's cool."

More ballsy: "Yeah, well, make sure you get the fuck gone. I'll call the police if you don't."

Enough ballsy. I walked quickly toward the back door of my apartment and, once inside, decided to call the police just in case my visitor decided to come back after all.

"What does he look like?" I gave a description to the precinct officer who answered the phone. "Is he still there?" I said I'd look out the kitchen window and the officer said he'd send a car by just in case he was still lurking around.

The backyard was deserted when I looked outside, but the gate to the alley was standing open. I walked out to close it and saw the garage door inside the yard was slightly open also. I pushed it all the way open and looked inside. The dome light in my car was on and there sat my visitor, rifling through the glove box, a joint burning in the ashtray as though he was taking a reefer break and decided as long as he was in the car, why not see if there was anything worth taking. To complete the relaxed scenario, he was humming a disjointed tune and low-talking to himself. Before he looked up and

285

saw me I heard him mumbling about that "stupid cracker mutha'fucker, actin' like he's gonna call the PO-lice. Shee-it, man, I coulda' dropped his ofay ass in a second but I decided to let him live and he's all 'I'll call the PO-lice.' Shoulda' capped the mutha'fucker. If I had a piece I woulda'. I gotta get me a snub." And, then he looked up. "Yo, man, goddam!" he bellowed. "You gotta stop sneakin' up on a dude. You scarin' me with that creepin' around shit."

"What the fuck are you doing in my car?" I pushed my hip against the car door to keep him in until the cops got there.

"Just takin' a break, man. That's all. No big deal. Ain't no place to sit that's comfortable in the street, man. Those bus benches are hard, hurt my ass, and with all those drug dealers runnin' around shootin' each other and shit, you know, dude could get hurt out there. You ain't got shit in here to steal, anyway. Except this nasty, dried out pack of Wrigley's gum. You know, this shit is made in Chicago, right here. Did you know that? That's where they get Wrigley Field. From the gum. All right, man, I'll get out your goddam car."

"I don't fucking believe this. You're still here after I said I was going to call the cops? Are you crazy? Do you want to go to jail?"

"Aw, man, jail ain't no big deal. Don't scare me not even a little."

He stepped out on the driver's side and I realized the pressure I had been putting on the passenger's side was more or less pointless. He side-scooted around the front of the car, obviously trying to get to the door. "You want a hit?" He held out the joint he'd been smoking. "It's some primo shit, man. One thing about these murderin' Jamaican mutha'fuckers. They got the best reef in the world, you know what I'm sayin'?

I can get you a lid, too, if you got some cash on you."

Just then, a loud voice from the front of the apartment building: "Mr. Malloy? Sir? Are you back there? Chicago police here. Hello?"

Reefer-man made it clear he was going out the back gate. "Well, ain't this a bitch! You did call the Po-lice. I thought you was bullshittin', man."

"I said I would. You're the dumb-ass who didn't believe me."

"Yeah, but white folks always be lyin' and shit. I thought you was just tryin' to scare me off."

"Well, surprise! Those cops out front are real."

"Mr. Malloy! Chicago police."

"Aw, man, tell 'em I'm gone. I didn't take nuthin' out your car. Here, I'll give you the rest of this joint." He pushed it into my hand. "Tell 'em I'm gone, man. For real. Do a dude a favor."

With that, he dissolved into the dark alley as completely as though he never existed.

Within seconds, one of Chicago's finest walked into the backyard. "Mr. Malloy? Officer Grizelli. You have a prowler? Precinct said you found someone on your property? Is that right?" He had that irritating habit of ending his questions with the last syllable two or three notes of the musical scale higher than the first.

"Yeah, some guy back here when I came home. Scared the hell out of me."

"Did he threaten you?" Up a note, which made the question sound like my visitor might have threatened someone else, a neighbor maybe, at 3:00 AM.

"No, didn't say a word. Maybe he came back here to take

a leak and I walked in on him. Anyway, looks like he's gone. Thanks for coming to check it out."

"Well, you never know. Especially in this neighborhood. The whole area is wall-to-wall drug dealers. Coulda' been one of them. And, they'll kill you as soon as look at you. Mean bastards, uh, people. Mean *people*. And foreigners. All of 'em. You know?" Up two notes.

"Well, he's gone so, lucky me, right?"

"Right." He paused a couple of beats. "Your name is Malloy?" Up two notes. "The new guy on the radio?" Up two notes.

"Uh, yeah. That's me." He dropped his head to his shoulder mic. "Hey, Stash. C'mon back here. It's the radio guy. The one who did that thing about walking stickers." He turned back to me. "Stash is my partner. You cracked us up down at the station house. That was some funny shit, excuse me, some funny *stuff*. We thought Daley would stroke on out when he heard about it. Did you catch hell, uh, get in trouble for that?" Up one note.

"Well, sort of. My boss wasn't happy, especially when Daley's office called him. I was just trying to be funny, you know."

Stash came into the backyard.

Officer Grizelli made the introductions. "This is the radio guy, Mike Malloy, and this is Officer Stashinski." We shook hands.

Stash's turn: "Hey, that was some funny stuff, the walking permits. We though Daley would stroke on out when he heard about it."

"I just told him that, Stash."

"Oh. Right. Hey, did you get rid of that hand gun? They're

illegal here, you know. Of course, that don't mean a thing to the bad guys. So, you had a prowler?"

"I thought I did. He said he was just cutting through my yard and stopped to take a leak and that's when I walked in. No big deal, I guess. Yeah, I got rid of the gun. Sorry you guys had to come out here."

"Hey, that's what they pay us the big bucks for, protect the public, right Stash?"

"That's it, man. But, I dunno what you've been drinkin' with the 'big bucks' stuff. I wish!"

"You mean 'what you've been smokin', not drinkin'."

"S'cuse me? Smokin? You know I don't smoke, Anthony."

"No, I mean what you said. It's 'what you been *smokin'* not *drinkin'*. That's the expression. You just got it wrong, partner."

This "Who's On First?" shit was seriously getting on my nerves. "Okay, guys. Thanks for coming out. I think it's all cool now. I don't want to hold you officers up . . . so to speak. There's probably all sorts of burglaries and muggings happening right now and I've got you two all tied up in this chit-chat. Plus, I'm tired. You know, just got off work, what? Three hours ago? Oh, my god it's 3:30 in the morning? I'm off to bed, guys. Thanks again."

Not yet.

"Stash" took out his note-pad. "Um, do you think I could have your autograph?" He thrust the pad at me. "Here's a pen, too. And lemme turn on my flashlight here, give you a little light."

Well, now I'm fucked because I still had burglar-man's half a joint in my hand. But, *thank you Jesus*, it was in my left hand. I write with my right. I took the pen and the pad, tucked the half-joint under my bent pinky, signed my fucking name, and handed it all back to "Stash." And watched in horror as the joint slid from under my finger and dropped to the ground.

"You dropped something, Mr. Malloy." Stash bent over to pick it up.

"Oh, that's okay, I'll get it. It's just a balled-up used Kleenex. *I'll get it."* Think. *Quick!* "Hey, did you hear something at the gate?" They both grabbed their holsters and turned to the back gate. I reached down, grabbed the goddam joint and pushed it into my pocket. "Oh, wait, I must be hearing shit. Naw, it's nothing, guys. My bad." They went to the back gate anyway and did a synchronized cop thing, looking up the alley and then down the alley, all serious like they'd been watching a lot of Hill Street Blues re-runs. Just then, Grizelli's shoulder mic beeped and I could hear the dispatch person telling them to go to an address on Sheridan where there was a "burglary in progress."

"Gotta go, Mr. Malloy! Got some trouble around the corner. Homeowner has a shotgun on some dude he found in his car! Precinct captain will get in touch with you for an incident report . . .!" That last shouted out the window as the car sped away in a cloud of burned rubber, blue light spinning, siren wailing. *Home owner has a shotgun pointed at someone he caught rifling through his car.* For a moment I wondered if it was joint-man. *My* burglar. Naw. Couldn't be. Dude couldn't be *that* stupid.

Chapter 24

Cicero

After three years in the Windy City, I knew it was time to leave Chicago and WLS when the PD accidentally emailed a nasty-ass, half-written memo to me rather than to the VP/General Manager to whom it was addressed. Most of it was missing but the part that got sent said, "*. . . I believe it's time to let Malloy go. His show is getting darker and darker and his attitude is so negative about the topics he discusses.*" His assessment of the tone of my show was absolutely correct. My attitude *was* dark and negative, but it was directed toward, and to a degree reflected, the madness that was consuming the legislative branch of the federal government. Washington was spiraling into a black hole of insane rhetoric that had one goal: The impeachment of Bill Clinton.

The collective raving and hysteria of the Republicans was becoming more and more unhinged. Clinton's crime, perjury about a blow-job from an adult woman who invited the President to engage in a bit of adulterous *le sexe oral*, was being compared in its criminality to the Nazi invasion of Poland; the crucifixion of Jesus; the treason of Benedict Arnold; anything and everything the congressional Republicans could dredge up from their encyclopedia of "worst things ever" to use against this goofy Elvis wannabe who, as president, had been running political circles around them and exposing them as the horses asses they really were. As a result, the dazed and confused Republicans were ecstatic when a recorded phone call was produced that clearly implicated this Elvis as having gotten his chicken choked by a rather voluptuous White House intern, a woman well into her twenties who had apparently decided that having the President of the United States ejaculating into her mouth and, oops, on her dress, was a once-in-a-lifetime opportunity so, what the fuck, let's do it. And, of course, Bill, being male, was incapable of honoring his marriage vows when an open, inviting, crimson-lipped mouth was waiting for his "uniquely marked" Johnson.

When Clinton subsequently was forced to testify about this sticky little event, he tried to do the honorable white Southern Man thing and protect the honor of the white Southern Woman, even though the woman in this goofy sexcapade was from California. He lied under oath. (This "white Southern woman honor and protection" bullshit could extend even to the point of murder if a black man were involved, no matter how remotely.) And it could have ended there. He would have successfully escaped an impeachable charge of perjury except for another of his suspected victim/playmates, a woman who wanted the world to know she, too, had been suckered into checking out Clinton's "odd-shaped penis" and, by god, the world would know about it because there is no fury like that of a Southern Belle who decides she was conned into giving it up to some smooth-talkin' married bastard who actually had no intention of leaving his missus and moving into a cozy double-wide out in the country where the two of them could live forever in red-neck bliss and Wednesday night prayer meetings. Now, by Jesus, she wants justice and some TV face time – and the fame that comes with it - just like that woman from California with the stained dress. Why should that snotty bitch get all the attention? The truth of Clinton's lie was exposed, the hell-gate of political lunacy was pushed wide open, and a chittering, foaming crowd of stunted demons came roiling out, all Republicans and all Christian hypocrites.

Clinton's House Republican tormentors did their best interpretations of shocked citizen-lawmakers when they presented the evidence for his removal from the presidency to the Senate during the subsequent trial. The most vocal of the prosecutors – an extraordinary number of the Christian Congressmen who were gleeful in sonorously stating their bullshit righteousness during their overheated presentations – were themselves adulterers who, in classic projection mode, found no problem in condemning ol' sax-playing Bill. It was a display of hypocrisy that set an entirely new standard of political destruction that may never be matched in its smarmy duplicity, all of which left me with the clear understanding that the political landscape of this dying republic, including the tone of the rhetoric and the emergence of Christian Fascism, would soon be littered with the shards of our experiment in democracy. That experiment had failed miserably even though the documents on which the whole thing rested were really cool. But, the balls of the Founders must have been the size of Massachusetts for having written the documents to begin with. A nation founded on slavery, racism, and genocide that insists it's all about equality under the law and the "rights of man," is a nation that eventually will commit suicide. After more than 200 years of demonstrating the inability of such freedoms and such rights to exist in a country that, in truth, worshipped above everything else the dehumanizing economic system known as Capitalism and its enforcer, Christianity, the writing for the end was indeed on the wall: *Mene, Mene, Tekel, Upsharin*, or, as interpreted by Daniel for the nervous King Belshazzar, *Numbered, numbered, weighed, divided.*

It was going to get even nastier, turbo-charged by the malignancy of the so-called Christian Right and the Republican Party's willingness to tear the country to pieces, if necessary, in order to impose their malignant style of racism, sexism, homophobia, and the absolute separation of Americans into a two-tiered economic system composed of the "haves" and the "have-nothings." So, was my on-air commentary getting darker and darker, and my attitude getting negative as my Program Director wrote in his mis-directed email? Yes, it was. However, at the same time, my program received the Chicago A.I.R. (Achievement in Radio) award, naming it the best night time radio talk show in the market. Oops. Apparently, I was not alone in the anger and disappointment that erupted from my program.

The real problem management was having was the number of complaints I was generating, all from a concerted effort of right-wing assholes who were not used to hearing anything other than the neo-Conservative gibberish (Limbaugh, Hannity, etc., etc.) that coated the nation with political slime, coast to coast, border to border, across the fruited plane. My style of progressive, liberal-left, talk was too much of a threat to the orderly fascistic bullshit they were brainwashed into believing was true, whether that bullshit was coming from the Catholic Church, the evangelical Protestants, or from the political right.

Taken together, this political and religious brainwashing was a double-barreled assault on reason, logical thinking, liberalism, and science. By continuing to do programming that garnered top ratings, I was able to survive the ideological assault up to a point. That point had a name: Michael Eisner, the CEO of Disney and therefore, *The Only Voice That Mattered* where it concerned radio stations owned and operated by ABC's parent company, Disney. The clutch of right-wing loons finally figured out the local bosses at WLS were not going to remove me unless I was caught doing something truly outrageous, like being caught in a motel room with a "live boy or a dead girl." The obvious solution was to go above – way above – local management. That meant Disney HQ in New York City.

My increasingly distraught PD said the station's General Manager wanted both of us in his office for a meeting. Oh, joy. Another sit-down with frightened, pissed off managers. I knew what to expect: The fear these men had incorporated into their working lives - whether Chicago or Atlanta – was palpable. Radio is not a career designed for stability. The rehab clinics and psychologist's offices have an abundance of clients, mostly male, who were chewed up by a business that lives and dies for ratings only, because ratings translate to money, profit, and market dominance which, in turn, generates more money and more profit, until the entire enterprise becomes so precariously balanced it can collapse as a result of even the smallest drop in the estimated number of listeners – estimated, because no one knows, no one has *ever* known the actual number of people tuning in to a particular station or a particular program. It was all based on bullshit generated by the radio ratings company Arbitron, a company soon to be swallowed up as a stand-alone operation, but still providing audience estimates that would determine who lived, who died, and who was to become a zombie.

The meeting was quick and to the point. The man with the title, VP/General Manager, was the first to speak. And the last. He set aside his busy-work when the PD and I walked in and looked up. At me.

"I never, ever want to get another phone call from Michael Eisner unless he is calling to offer me a promotion. Is that clear? Do we understand each other?"

"Well, I . . . "

"Do we understand each other?"

"Yes, sir. Yes, we do. Very clear."

"Thank you. That's all." And it was.

The PD and I walked back to his office. "One question, boss. What did the demi-god, the sanctified Mr. Eisner, say to our illustrious leader? Must have scared the shit outta him."

"I have no idea," he said. "But, if I were you, I'd stop doing whatever it is you're doing that rattles Eisner's cage. This is Major Market radio, man, the number three market in the country. It's not a home-town station like the one you came from in Atlanta. It's part of a corporate behemoth that generates tens of billions of dollars a year in revenue and it's managed by Masters of the Universe who have no idea who you are or why you work for part of the company. And, they don't care if you live or die. Until Eisner got whatever phone call or email that triggered his wrath, your name was only one of billions. Now, if he hears it again he will wave his corporate death ray and you will no longer exist. I hope Zemira (the VP) made that point."

"Death ray? What did I do to ensure the next time I did it

would be fatal? This is some crazy shit."

"Don't take it literally, for Christ's sake. But, professionally? Once someone like Michael Eisner puts the evil eye on you, you might want to find another career. Maybe something like commercial fishing in Alaska, something far away that will kill any idea you might have of getting back into radio."

"So, okay, now, what did I do? That's what I started to ask Zemira."

"It doesn't matter."

"Then how the fuck am I supposed to stop doing it if I don't know what the fuck I've done?"

"I don't know either. Zemira is a man of few words and he didn't give me specifics."

"This is crazy, man. Seriously."

"No, it's A-M radio. Crazy is what it produces."

Later that night, after a very subdued program that featured my interview with the Director of The Chicago Youth Symphony, I got in the car and headed for Lakeshore Drive and home. I stopped at a light and all of a sudden, a guy was tapping on my driver's side window. It was 2 o'clock in the morning. I rolled the window down.

"Yeah . . .?"

"I'm sorry to bother you, sir, honest to god, but I've got a bad situation here and just a little assistance is all I need. I'm not a hold-up man. I'm just trying to get home and, see that car up there . . .?"

He pointed to a car pulled to the side of Michigan Avenue. The emergency lights were blinking, and the front driver's side door was open.

"That's my car. I don't know what's wrong with it, it just stopped, and I've got to get home. I live in Cicero and with a little help I can get a tow truck to come get my car and I can get home. My wife's at her mother's in Indiana and our ten-year-old is home all alone. Could you help me?"

He was wearing brown slacks, neatly pressed, and a checkered sport coat over a white shirt, the collar open and the knot of his tie pulled down onto his shirt. This was definitely not a thug.

"What do you need?"

"Well, the tow will cost about a hundred dollars and I've collected about ten and I've got, I think, another twenty on me. That's all I took when I left home. When I come into the city I don't carry a lot of cash, too risky. A person can get mugged here. Whatever you can spare I'll pay you back." He handed me a small notebook and the stub of a pencil. "Just put your name and address under that other name and I promise I'll send it." He looked like he was about to cry.

I took the notebook, wrote my name and address, and handed back the pad, the pencil, and seventeen dollars I pulled out of my pocket. "Thank you, thank you, sir. I promise you'll get this back. Now, you're . . ." He read my name and address aloud, as if committing it to memory.

I drove away, knowing I had done a good deed. It seemed like I hadn't done one for a long time and I had that feeling Mark Twain described as how you felt when Sunday morning church was finally over, the benediction had been recited, the hymnals closed, and folks were walking out into the glorious morning sunshine, their souls cleansed, their guilt washed away in the blood of the Lamb.

Three weeks later, after working out my separation agreement with WLS, I was once again driving back to Rogers Park late at night when I saw him. Same well-dressed man, except this time he was wearing a black fedora a little too small for his head. He was standing on a traffic island near a stoplight on Michigan Avenue. I drove slowly so I would get to him just as the light turned red. He didn't recognize me, but, then, why should he? I was just a passing Good Samaritan. He approached the car.

"Sir? Hi, I know this is crazy, but I really need some help. See that car over there?" He pointed to a car sitting against the curb, the emergency lights blinking, the rear passenger's side door open.

"Uh-huh. Yeah, I see it."

"Well, it just stopped on me, and I live in the western suburbs, Bolingbrook actually, and I'm trying to get home. My wife's in Indiana taking care of her sick mom and my ten-year-old is home alone waiting for me. I want to call a tow truck but that'll cost about a hundred dollars and I don't have that on me. I never bring much cash when I come into the city because, you know, you can get mugged here."

All I could think was, *Jeezis Fucking Kee-rist.* This guy needs some variation to his script. Maybe more than just one script or even some sort of disguise to avoid what was about to happen. Just wearing a hat didn't cut it.

"So, how much do you need?"

"Well, like I said, a hundred will do it and I've got about twenty, so anything will help. And, you can write your name and address in my notepad here and I'll mail it back to you, and that's a promise!" He held out the notepad and a stubby pencil. It was a list of names. Somewhere on that list was my name. This was too fucking weird.

"I thought you lived in Cicero."

"What? Excuse me?"

"The last time we played this little game you said you lived in Cicero. Did you move? Get a better place? Business is good?"

"Uh . . ." He started to back away. "I don't know what you mean. I've always lived in Bolingbrook."

"Really? What, am I confusing you with some other punk? Where's my motherfucking seventeen dollars? Your ten-year-old still home alone?"

All at once . . . recognition!

"Aww, man, you're that guy from a couple of weeks ago, right?" He kept pitching. "I said I'd pay you back and I will." His eyes were darting up and down the now deserted Magnificent Mile. "That's my car over there." He pointed to the sedan with the blinking emergency lights. "I'll go get your money, man, and then we're square." And he started running for the car. To get my money? Not even. He jumped behind the wheel and took off, tires squealing, rear passenger door slamming shut, and, as a gesture of enduring utter contempt from the con man to the mark, he gave me the finger. And then he leaned out the window and screamed, *"Fuck you, asshole!"*

That hurt my feelings. So, I floored the Altima and took off after him. He cut across one of the side streets and headed north on Clark Street. There was no traffic and we both were driving like we were running moonshine in the north Georgia mountains. At least I was. We fish-tailed into the Lincoln Park neighborhood, past the Moody Bible Institute, the Newberry Library, what used to be the garage made famous for the Valentine's Day Massacre, a totally crazed, night-time, high-speed tour past three Chicago landmarks, which is not how I wanted to spend one of my last Friday nights in the city Carl Sandburg found so "stormy, husky, brawling . . "

He was pulling away. He knew the neighborhood better than

I did and I was getting concerned about what would happen if I did catch him. Dying over seventeen dollars didn't seem like an idea with an upside. Fuck it. Keep my money, shit-head, and may you die of a hideous disease that wracks your body with unbearable pain and makes you scream for mercy. Okay, that's a bit severe. Forget the "unbearable pain" part. I cut over to Broadway, found a parking spot, and went into the Green Mill for a drink. Later that night - maybe caused by the drinks I had at the Mill, a favorite hangout of Al Capone's back in the day - I had an unsettling dream, unsettling because it was so lucid. It began in a place of total ruin . . .

There he is again. Dark suit. Black turtleneck. Standing in the night's deep shadows, leaning against the building's buttress. Still smoking his smelly Gitanes. As always, he is staring at me with that irritating, quizzical look. Every time I see him, every time he manages to materialize in front of me, that look. How is he able to do that? Materialize. Not here; then here. No matter where I find myself, he is there, waiting. As is his custom, no hello. Just right to the point. "So, who is it this time?" he asks, with an exasperated tone, as if I were a child pulling his sleeve for attention.

"Oh, shit! You again. Don't you get tired of this? Always showing up, always the same question: 'Who is it this time?' Look, why don't you just disappear? You know, vanish. Poof!"

With his carefully manicured forefinger he taps the ash off his cigarette. "Now, that's just so ungrateful, you know? In the first place, I wouldn't even be here except for your homicidal tendencies. So, who is it this time? What poor schmuck finally made it to the top of your list? Anybody I know?" He steps out of the clotted shadows into the circle of pale street light splashed on the pavement like a drying puddle of after-party vomit.

"Yeah, you know him. I've been following this creep for hours. It

took forever just to get this close. And I'm exhausted. I need some sleep."

He laughs. "That's pretty ironic. You need some sleep. What do you think this is?" He waves his arm in a semi-circle.

What is it? It's a black landscape of misshapen, leafless trees, skeletal buildings, dead animals, and a night punctured with high-pitched shrieks and squeals, and the reason he's here is to stop me. I've been through this before and this time I won't let him interfere.

"I'll make you a deal," I say to him. "I'm gonna walk down this street a few blocks, just checking out the terrain, so to speak. You wait here, and I promise nothing will happen. Then, I'll come back, and we can talk about how to get rid of you. Fair?"

He crushes the cigarette under his heel and lights another one. "So, you want me to trust you? Is that what you're suggesting?"

"Yes."

He stares at me, sizing up what I am saying. He takes a silent inhale and blows out a cloud of black smoke. For a moment I can't see him. Then, he is standing next to me, too close. "Down the street and back, right?"

"Right."

"Okay. This one time. Let's see if you are trustworthy."

Bullshit. Anything to get this asshole out of my way. He steps back into the crumbling building's shadows, the tip of his cigarette glowing bright, dim, bright, like a slowly flashing light on an emergency vehicle.

I walk down a street that is dark and wide. It must have been a main thoroughfare at one time with cars and office buildings and noise and crowds of people pushing this way and that. Now, it's an empty, broad path through a place filled with shifting shapes, moving shadows. It is well past midnight, if midnight exists here.

On both sides of the street the buildings that must have been here are gone, replaced by small, oddly shaped structures that tilt, structures with glassy-eyed windows that seem to be blinking in the watery light leaking from bent street-lamps. There's an axe in my hand. It is heavy, like the head of a sledgehammer. The effort it takes to carry it makes my breathing uneven. I keep walking, shifting it from left hand to right. Then I see him again, the one I have been following in this god-forsaken landscape. He is walking a half-block ahead of me with a slow, arrogant stride, his large head slightly cocked, a strut that projects malignant narcissism. He must die. Tonight. Right now. That's why I am here.

It takes a few minutes to catch up to him. I move slowly, forcing my feet through a resistance that feels like wet sand. His long, dark overcoat is turned up at the collar, the coat's hem dragging through the thick debris covering the broken street. He is mumbling, repeating the same guttural sounds over and over. He slows his pace. He stops and slowly, arrogantly, turns to face me. A ridiculously long red tie is knotted perfectly around his neck. I can see his pursed lips, his florid face. It is him. I lunge, the axe raised over my head. He lifts his hand and knocks away its downward arc, grabbing and twisting my wrists, causing me to stumble in to his bulky body. I see the axe sliding away, into the gutter. His arms tighten around my torso, pulling me into a rigid embrace. His face is level with mine. His eyes are empty holes. His hot breath stinks, a greasy smell of hamburgers, French fries, catsup. He is holding me so tightly I can't gag. He lifts me off the street. I cannot move. He tightens his grip until I cannot breathe. I try to push away from his bulk. No use. I manage to free one arm and lift it to grab his yellow hair, to try to push my thumb into his eye, to do something, anything, to break his rigid grip. He holds a length of rope, thick, as if ripped from an anchor. He releases his grip, but I cannot move

303

any part of my body. I am paralyzed. He puts the rope around my neck and pulls it tight, closing my throat. I know I am going to die. I try to scream, the sound weak and pointless, just loud enough to cause the hairless creatures hiding in the gutter to run, squealing and shrieking.

His dead eyes, suddenly the color of hell, burn into mine and he begins a grunting laugh, his viscous spittle spraying my face. His mumbled chanting is suddenly clear: " Build the wall! No collusion! No collusion!" over and over. The rope is drawn tighter and I fade to nothing.

I force my eyes open. They're sticky. The bed is damp with sweat. Pale daylight, filtered through an early Chicago morning rain, fills the bedroom, soaking it with anxiety. Damn! That was intense. A nightmare filled with doom. I have no explanation for it. I hadn't recently seen a horror flick. I hadn't read a scary novel. So, what did it mean? The red tie; what was that? The dark overcoat, the blond hair, the axe. The ruined, dark landscape. I had no idea. I raise the glass of water by the bedside and swallow several large mouthfuls. And, before his image fades, I wonder why the man smoking the Gitanes didn't help me.

Three weeks later I packed a U-Haul with my accumulated detritus and said good-bye and thanks for all the fish to the city made famous, in part, because of how many swine had been "butchered" and changed into pork chops, hams, bacon and other edible pig parts and how much wheat had been "stacked." Me? I knew my memories of Chicago would always be fucked up.

I slid a Pink Floyd CD into the player and began the long drive back to Atlanta.

About the Author

MIKE MALLOY has been a radio talk show host for the past 35 years. Prior to radio, Mike was a writer/producer for CNN in the early 1980s. Additionally, he has worked as a writer, editor and columnist for various Atlanta publications.

His program was voted Best Talk Show in both New York City and Chicago by A.I.R. – the Achievement in Radio organization - the only radio talk show host to be so awarded in both the first and third largest markets in the country.

He has been heard on two "heritage" radio stations, WLS-AM in Chicago, WSB-AM in Atlanta, as well as national syndication by Air America Radio.

He lives in Atlanta, Georgia with his wife of 22 years, Kathy, and 14-year-old daughter, Molly.

CPSIA information can be obtained
at www.ICGtesting.com
Printed in the USA
FSHW022132090519